Lincoln Electric

a history

VIRGINIA P. DAV

THE LINCOLN ELECTRIC COMPANY
CLEVELAND, OHIO

ACKNOWLEDGMENT

LINCOLN ELECTRIC expresses its thanks to the members of the Lincoln family for their leadership of the company and for their encouragement to proceed with this project. The company is also pleased that Virginia Dawson, Ph.D., found the time and energy to author this history. Finally, Lincoln Electric acknowledges the Winthrop Group, Inc., Cambridge, Mass., for its role as a catalyst in commencing this project in the first part of this decade.

Lincoln Electric: A History

Virginia P. Dawson

Produced by History Enterprises, Inc.
11000 Cedar Avenue, Cleveland, Ohio 44106
in collaboration with the Winthrop Group, Inc.

Library of Congress Catalogue Card Number 95-80209
ISBN Number: 0-937392-01-4

Design by Dix & Eaton Incorporated

Lincoln Electric

a history

Contents

Introduction

This is the story of The Lincoln Electric Company, founded in 1895 by John Cromwell Lincoln. At a time of unusual opportunity and risk for young entrepreneurs, John Lincoln found customers for his electric motors during one of the severest economic depressions of the previous century. His dissatisfaction with the inequities of

Facing page: The Lincoln Electric Company's baseball team circa 1907. John Lincoln stands in the back row, center. James Lincoln kneels in his Ohio State University letter sweater.

late-nineteenth century capitalism and his encounter with social reformers like Cleveland Mayor Tom Johnson and the writings of economist Henry George changed the focus of his life. Lincoln gave up management of Lincoln Electric to become an advocate for a single tax as the means to bring about a more equitable distribution of wealth.

John Lincoln's sense of mission and democratic ideals would live on in the incentive philosophy of his brother, James Finney Lincoln. J. F. Lincoln was destined to become a legendary figure, not only within the company, but also within the ranks of American managers. He presided over the metamorphosis of The Lincoln Electric Company from a small shop producing electric motors into a formidable competitor in the electric arc welding field. Energetic, forceful and articulate, Lincoln had the messianic zeal of an Old Testament prophet. He thought the company could contribute to both material and moral progress. Just as arc welding would bring about a revolution in the way metals were joined, thereby raising the world's standard of living, a new approach to management would usher in a new age in industry.

For Lincoln the essence of good management was expressed in the Golden Rule – treat others as you would like to be treated. J. F. Lincoln had the ability to inspire people at all levels of the company: "When he got up in a company meeting and began by saying: 'Fellow Workers,' he meant just that, and a blush of pride rippled through the audience," the company's former traffic manager recalled.[1] J. F. Lincoln's "incentive management system" promised to establish harmony between labor and management and provide social mobility for workers. He envisioned a classless society where all shared a progressively higher standard of living. Like Henry Ford, he preached greater standardization and mass production as the key to progress. The Lincoln Electric Company focused on manufacturing a better product for more people at a lower cost. It passed cost reductions on to customers in lower prices.

Incentive management helped make Lincoln Electric among the world's most admired and studied manufacturing corporations of our era. J. F. Lincoln's approach to management grew out of a compelling philosophy of the perfectibility of human beings, grounded in the practical rule that people work better when they are rewarded for their efforts. The uniqueness of Lincoln Electric's incentive system has made it the subject of both academic investigation and popular articles from the 1940s to the present. In the early 1990s, the company received wide media attention. A CBS television special, "Ethics in American Business," focused on Lincoln Electric's policy of no layoffs. In a business environment where workers were regarded as expendable commodities, Lincoln Electric workers could be confident they had a job for life. An officer of the company told Walter Cronkite, "Laying off workers is not only unethical, it is bad business." He explained that when you lose

workers and are forced to hire and train new people, the result is lower productivity and quality. Hiring and retaining good workers contributes to a strong bottom line. "The McNeil/Lehrer Report" and "60 Minutes" highlighted Lincoln Electric's strong entrepreneurial culture. Lincoln workers manage themselves, averaging one foreman for every one hundred employees. They have no paid sick days or holidays and accept mandatory overtime. Factory workers are paid for what they produce and defective work must be corrected on an employee's own time. These television documentaries emphasized that pay for performance and accountability – new concepts for many companies in the early 1990s – have been practiced at Lincoln Electric for more than fifty years.

Incentive management is the reason for the company's legendary productivity and stature in the business community. The goal of incentive management is to maximize efficiency by motivating workers to work quickly and accurately. J. F. Lincoln considered piecework an essential element of the system. Since workers are paid for the number of pieces they produce, they control the pace of work and know exactly how much money they are making. The system encourages innovation since workers are constantly on the lookout for ways to speed up production. A retired employee calculated that he had coated more than 200 million pounds of welding wire during his thirty-seven-year career working in the electrode division. His job had required vigilance and stamina, and he recalled his work with pride. "You know there's little tricks," he said, "and you have to always be looking. I can walk into a wire room and in five minutes I can see what they're doing wrong."[2]

Looking for ways to promote efficiency is not limited to factory workers. It has always been a way of life at Lincoln Electric. In addition to the incentive provided by piecework, a year-end bonus motivates workers to find ways to cut costs and increase productivity. A former secretary recalled the culture shock she experienced when she first came to Lincoln Electric during World War II and learned there were no coffee breaks and she had to furnish her own pencils. At first she found this penny-pinching peculiar, but soon she saw the relation between her behavior and the bonus all employees shared each year. "Pretty soon you're doing the same thing," she said, "because you know that your bonus depends on saving money."[3] Regular take-home pay for workers has always been comparable to that of other industrial workers in Cleveland, but the cash bonus that the company pays out of the profits of the company each year is unusual. From the end of World War II through the early 1980s, the bonus often increased Lincoln workers' take-home pay by more than 100 percent. The bonus was never an entitlement, but a reward for efficient production and low overhead. An employee handbook from the 1970s stated, "The bonus, paid at the discretion of the company, is not a gift, but rather it is the sharing of the results of efficient operation on the basis of the contribution of each person to the success of the company for that year."[4]

Although the bonus has long been the most recognizable feature of Lincoln's incentive management, it is only one element of a system that evolved over time to create the company's unique corporate culture. J. F. Lincoln always stressed that workers were the company's greatest asset. Fear of layoffs, in his view, dampened workers' motivation. He instituted the policy of "guaranteed continuous employment" in the 1950s. The knowledge that they will never be laid off continues to encourage employee loyalty and flexibility and pushes management to find innovative ways to keep the work force on the job during industrial slumps.

Along with the story of the company's remarkable incentive system, Lincoln Electric's history is closely connected with the growth of arc welding in the United States. Indeed, though the incentive system has been the subject of scholarly attention and has consistently received publicity, the company's role in shaping the field of arc welding in the United States is even more significant from a historical point of view. Arc welding is a process that makes bonding any type of metal cheaper, faster, and stronger. It is particularly important in steel fabrication. When a spark jumps the gap between a metallic electrode and a metal work piece and completes an electric circuit, it produces an intense heat that melts both the electrode and the metal pieces to be joined. They form a bond as strong or stronger than the original metal. Before World War I, arc welding had only limited applications. It was used, for example, to fill holes in defective castings, repair steam boilers, and mend the riveted hulls of the ships that plied the Great Lakes. Prior to the 1920s, it was generally accepted that cast iron was superior to welded steel and that riveting was the only way to safely and securely join metals.

Incentive management is the reason for the company's legendary productivity and stature in the business community.

The Lincoln Electric Company's promotion of arc welding in the 1920s and 1930s contributed to changing that perception. The company's profits grew as the field of arc welding grew, transforming the design and construction of buildings, bridges, ships, and industrial machinery. During World War II the construction of Liberty Ships, tanks, bombs, and other armaments

created enormous demand for arc welding products. After the war, the revolution anticipated by J. F. Lincoln finally came. Arc welding replaced riveting in most forms of metal fabrication, while at the same time the mass production of electrodes by a work force motivated to achieve cost reductions turned The Lincoln Electric Company into an enormously efficient and profitable enterprise. During the Eisenhower era's drive to create a national highway system, graceful arc welded-bridges became symbols of the acceptance of arc welding as a mature industry. Today in the United States arc welding is no longer a growth industry. However, recognition of its unlimited potential in parts of the world that are still developing industrial economies prompted the company to make acquisitions outside the United States. As an international company, The Lincoln Electric Company now manufactures and sells arc welding products not only in the United States, but also in Latin America, Asia, and Europe.

The transformation of Lincoln Electric into a global company came at a price.

The transformation of Lincoln Electric into a global company came at a price. Between 1986 and 1992 Lincoln Electric rapidly expanded from a company with five manufacturing plants – in Euclid and Mentor, Ohio; Canada; Australia; and France – to twenty-two plants in fifteen countries. Almost immediately, the new acquisitions in Europe and Latin America proved to be liabilities. In 1992, while the company's domestic operations remained strongly profitable, losses from its acquisitions in other parts of the world steadily mounted. This situation presented the management of the company with an agonizing ethical and strategic dilemma that struck at the heart of Lincoln's incentive system. Lincoln workers expected the bonus they thought they had earned through the continued outstanding efficiency of American operations. Conventional wisdom and professional judgment suggested eliminating the bonus. Management and the board of directors, however, opted to borrow the funds needed to pay the bonus.

Why management made this decision to continue to pay the bonus despite the company's losses reflects the power of Lincoln Electric's corporate culture and the value that management places on the contributions of each individual to the company's success. Between the 1930s and the early 1990s the company's management system did not change very much, but the drive to become a global company precipitated long-overdue changes at Lincoln Electric. The uncertainty created by the company's acquisitions had eroded the foundation of trust between Lincoln's management and its workers. Strongly profitable again, in 1996 the company began a process of self-examination that led to the reform and reaffirmation of the incentive system. The "incentive performance system" instituted in 1997 represents an updated version of incentive management, appropriate for a company of Lincoln Electric's size and complexity and adapted to the business realities of the late-twentieth century. A new formula-based method of computing the bonus encourages continuous improvement through both individual and company-wide performance incentives. These incentives apply to Lincoln Electric's companies around the world, creating a unified company bound by common goals.

A sense of mission expresses the book's two themes. The first is the Lincoln brothers' commitment to a democratic form of capitalism that resulted in the creation and evolution of the company's unique system of incentive management. The other theme is the company's mission to win the acceptance of arc welding as a basic metal fabrication process. Chapter 1 deals with John Lincoln and the founding and early years of the company, placing them in the context of Cleveland's history. John Lincoln was a prolific inventor who got his start in Cleveland in the arc lighting and electric traction business. In the early years Lincoln motors and battery-chargers for electric automobiles were the company's staple products. Values that transcended the workaday world led John Lincoln to give up active management of Lincoln Electric. Chapter 2 describes the evolution of the company after J. F. Lincoln took over. He focused the company on arc welding and worked to win acceptance of arc welding as a basic metal fabrication process. At the same time he also expressed his sense of mission through the development of incentive management. Though few records of the company's early history have survived, J. F. Lincoln's writings and other company publications sketch both the evolution of his management system and his efforts to advance the field of arc welding.

The period between 1929 and the end of World War II is the subject of Chapter 3. The Great Depression, a time when scores of companies in Cleveland failed, proved a turning point in the history of Lincoln Electric. The reason was twofold: the introduction of a coated or shielded electrode called Fleetweld® and the payment of the first significant Lincoln bonus. During a period of militant labor organizing and violent strikes, J. F. Lincoln's bonus proved not only generous, but astute. It deflected any interest Lincoln Electric workers might have had in unions. The creation of the James F. Lincoln Arc Welding Foundation and an aggressive publication program advanced the field of arc welding at the same time that it helped to sell Lincoln products during the Depression.

Chapter 4 describes the publicity J. F. Lincoln garnered both in defending the incentive system against the government, and by allowing it to be studied by the first contingent of Harvard Business

School professors. Unlike Lincoln Electric's competitors that produced either welding equipment or electrodes (called "consumables" because they are used up in the welding process), The Lincoln Electric Company promoted arc welding as a process by selling both equipment and consumables. Loyal customers came to depend on the Lincoln sales engineer not only for high-quality arc-welding products, but also for welding expertise.

Manufacturing and company management in the postwar period up to the death of J. F. Lincoln is the subject of Chapter 5. It describes initiatives taken by some of the talented individuals personally recruited by J. F. Lincoln. This chapter also deals with the challenge of Innershield®, a new flux-cored electrode, developed in response to the threat posed by gas-shielded arc welding.

Chapter 6 discusses the management of the company under Lincoln's successor, William Irrgang, whose intense loyalty to Lincoln's ideas eventually became counterproductive. In the early years, J. F. Lincoln had pragmatically modified his management theories, but his strong personality and longevity produced a management culture that revered his management philosophy to a fault. A Harvard Business School case study in 1975 emphasized the continuity of the management philosophy.[5] By choice Lincoln Electric remained a company that manufactured a few products extremely efficiently and sold most of them domestically. With the exception of the development of Innershield, the company's products did not change very much between the 1930s and the 1980s. Nor did its unique management system, despite a serious recession in the early 1980s.

The book's final chapter discusses how The Lincoln Electric Company became an international company. The company's drive for acquisitions around the globe touched off a tumultuous decade of change under the leadership of George Willis and later Donald Hastings. It ended with a successful global strategy set in place by the current chief executive officer and chairman of the board, Anthony Massaro. If globalization created anomalies and stresses in the incentive system that had served the company so well for so long, ultimately new leadership produced a stronger, more flexible management system that preserved the spirit of J. F. Lincoln's ideas.

Numerous management studies published from the 1940s to the present provided an invaluable starting point for my research. What my history adds to these important contributions to management literature is greater focus on the technology of arc welding and how it influenced the management of the company. I also examine the history of Lincoln Electric's management system within the context of welfare capitalism. Most historical work on welfare capitalism assumes that it was a movement that failed with the coming of the Great Depression. A new book on postwar welfare capitalism, *Modern Manors: Welfare Capitalism Since the New Deal* by Sanford Jacoby, argues that welfare capitalism continued after World War II, but the companies that practiced different forms of the employer-sponsored benevolence have not received the attention they deserve.[6] The Lincoln Electric Company shares many similarities with the three companies that Jacoby has studied: Kodak, Sears, and Thompson Products, making its system less unusual than previously thought.

In general, besides promotional literature and management studies, sources for the history of the company were disappointing. The company archives consist of publications, as well as a few unusual primary sources and hundreds of photographs that document the history of arc welding. I have referenced this material as "LEC archives." I also used a collection of early letters between John and James Lincoln, drafts of James Lincoln's letters to the editors of Cleveland newspapers, and his correspondence with J. L. Morrill, vice president of Ohio State University in the 1930s. These letters are referenced as "Papers of Harry Carlson, Jr." In addition, the Papers of Harry Carlson, Jr. contain family genealogy, old advertisements, photographs, and early company publications. I had access to the minutes of the meetings of the board of directors and the Advisory Board minutes through the 1970s. For the final chapters of the book I relied on interviews with company executives Anthony Massaro, George Willis, Donald Hastings, Frederick Stueber, Ray Vogt, Jay Elliott, John Stropki, and Frederick Mackenbach as well as newspaper articles and other published material.

The James F. Lincoln Papers at the Western Reserve Historical Society yielded little about the day-to-day management of the company. However, I found useful information on the A. O. Smith and Linde patent cases and Renegotiation during World War II. These papers contain press clippings, pamphlets, proceedings of the public hearings, patent disputes, and memorabilia. The Ohio State University archives provided documentation of J. F. Lincoln's alumni activities, and the Oberlin College archives made available material relating to William E. Lincoln, father of John and James. Wooster College archives provided information on the founding of the Council of Profit Sharing Industries. I also received help from the Profit Sharing/401(k) Council of America, located in Chicago. Kathryn Lincoln forwarded notes assembled by John Love for a Lincoln biography, *The American Century of John C. Lincoln* (1962) by Raymond Moley, a member of Franklin D. Roosevelt's "braintrusters" and close advisor to the Lincoln Foundation, Inc. The best sources for the company's management philosophy remain James F. Lincoln's three books, *Lincoln's Incentive System* (1946), *Incentive Management* (1951), and *A New Approach to Industrial Economics* (1961).

The first draft of this book was completed in October 1994. In 1998 the manuscript was reorganized and rewritten, as well as redesigned. I would like to thank most heartily David Lincoln and Harry Carlson, Jr., for their insights and tireless advocacy of this history. I am also grateful to

Richard Sabo, who initiated it in anticipation of the company's centennial, and Roy Morrow, who saw it through to completion. I would also like to thank Charlotte Filby, who assisted in ways too numerous to count.

I am grateful to my former colleague, Davis Dyer, for his advice and encouragement during the time that the Lincoln Electric history was a project of the Winthrop Group. Charles Herbruck also served as a consultant during the project's early phases and provided valuable critiques. Arthur Todd (deceased) shared his first-hand knowledge and enthusiasm for the history of the company. Frances Bayless searched Fairmount Presbyterian Church records and Meg Sondey sent me an unpublished paper on arc welding. Noreen Carlozzi helped check facts, and Jenny Ogborn assisted in culling photos from the company's voluminous collection. The following current and former employees and members of the board graciously consented to be interviewed: Eileen Aranda, Omer Blodgett, Harry Carlson, Jr., Mrs. George Clipsham, Jay Elliott, Proctor Ferris, Preston Few, Donald Hastings, Charles Herbruck, Jerry Hinkel, Kathleen Hoenigman, Brian Jackson, Paul Jerabek, Joe Kernya, Harry Larkins, David Lincoln, Frederick Mackenbach, Neal Manross, Anthony Massaro, William Miskoe, Howard Morris, John Murray, Quentin Ponder, Louis Prebevsek, Howard Reinke, Jean Revelt, David Ross, Richard Sabo, William Schuster, Roland Sharer, Robert Shutt, Ellis Smolik, Harry K. Smith, L. Keever Stringham, John Stropki, Frederick Stueber, Arthur Todd, Richard Ulstad, Joseph Vinceller, Ray Vogt, Helen White, and George Willis. Finally, I would like to thank my Lincoln Electric Welding School instructors who taught me the mysteries of striking an arc, and Helen White with whom I shared many a lunch in the Lincoln cafeteria while this book was in the making.

---

1 Communication from Arthur W. Todd to author, "On the Quality of Leadership" no date.

2 Interview with Louis Prebevsek, July 21, 1994.

3 Interview with Helen G. White, Feb. 15, 1992.

4 Norman Berg and Norman Fast, "The Lincoln Electric Company," (Harvard Business School, Case 376-028, 1975), 5.

5 Berg and Fast, 13.

6 Sanford M. Jacoby, *Welfare Capitalism Since the New Deal* (Princeton: Princeton University Press, 1997).

Chapter 1

Staking Out a Place in the Electrical Industry, 1895-1914

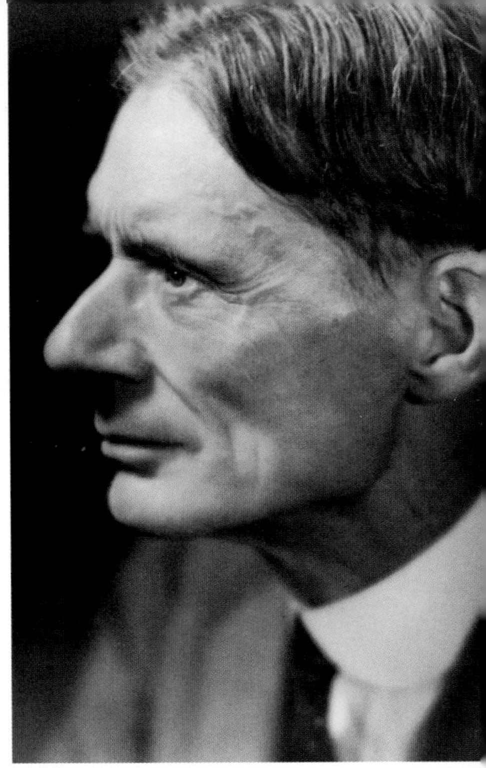

John C. Lincoln, 1866-1959, founder of The Lincoln Electric Company

When John Lincoln took up residence in Cleveland in 1888, it was a city on the move. Giant barges loaded with iron ore from the Lake Superior region of Michigan drew up to docks at the mouth of the Cuyahoga River to be unloaded by mechanical hoists recently introduced by the Brown Hoisting & Conveying Machinery Company. Railroad cars loaded with coal from the Appalachian range in Ohio, Indiana, and Illinois converged on the steel mills, the backbone of the industrialization of the Midwest. They belched black smoke that covered the city with a daytime haze. At night the yellow glare from the blast furnaces of the steel mills lit up the sky. In downtown Cleveland, Public Square was ablaze with Charles Brush's arc lights. It was a time of opportunity for inventors seeking practical applications for electricity, a dynamic new industry. During the previous decade, inventions related to arc-lighting by Charles Brush and Elihu Thomson, as well as Thomas Edison's development of an incandescent lighting system, had inaugurated the field of electric lighting and power generation.

An arc light is produced by arcing a current across a gap between the ends of two pieces of carbon. As the electric current jumps the gap between the carbon electrodes, it produces an arc of intense light. When Sir Humphry Davy gave one of the first public demonstrations of the arc light in 1808 in London, it received current from a battery of 2,000 cells. Dramatic as this demonstration was, as long as batteries provided the source of current, the arc light remained a laboratory curiosity, too expensive for commercial application. The discovery of electromagnetic induction by Michael Faraday in 1831 held the promise of producing electricity less expensively with a dynamo. By the 1870s, with developments by the Belgian inventor, Zenobe Theophile Gramme, and the American, Edward Weston, the dynamo became a practical method to produce direct current electricity. Dynamos were first used by Gramme and Weston in the electroplating industry.[1]

Charles Brush, John C. Lincoln's future employer, realized the commercial potential of the dynamo. Brush's arc-lighting system dominated the field through innovations that included an automatic regulator to maintain a constant current and an automatic carbon feeder. The system's design was simple enough for easy repair. In 1875 Brush built one of the first systems of electric lighting in the world on Public Square in downtown Cleveland.[2] The Brush Electric Company enjoyed phenomenal growth. By 1885 Brush's factory in Cleveland had the capacity to produce 1,500 lamps per month, with about 80,000 lamps in service in principal American cities.[3] However, it was not long before able competitors in the arc-lighting field, along with the success of Edison's newer system of incandescent lighting, began to drive him out of business. Incandescent lighting offered the advantage of practical interior lighting and central power stations for the generation and distribution of electricity. Though the arc light rapidly became obsolete, the related technology of arc welding would serve as the foundation for a new method of metal fabrication. The day would come when arc welding would transform the production of industrial machinery, consumer goods, and twentieth century building construction.

Since the electric arc generates tremendous heat (up to 5,000° F), it was noted soon after the invention of the arc light that it could be used to melt and bond metals. In France Auguste De Meritens joined lead plates for storage batteries using the heat of an arc in about 1884. Shortly afterwards, his pupil, Nikolai N. Benardos, a Russian, received the first patent for carbon arc welding with his colleague Stanislaus Olszewaski. In 1889 a demonstration at the Paris Exposition provoked interest in using the process to repair steam boilers. The following year Charles Lewis Coffin of Detroit received the first American patent for the metal arc-welding process.[4] About the same time, Elihu Thomson, Brush's old competitor in the arc-lighting business, patented a process for resistance welding. But electric arc welding did not come into widespread use in metal fabrication until it could be made a practical, versatile and relatively inexpensive method to join

The day would come when arc welding would transform the production of industrial machinery, consumer goods, and twentieth century building construction.

metals. John C. Lincoln played a role in the transformation of arc welding into a viable commercial process. His inventions in the new field of electricity laid the foundation for the company's future profitability.

MODEST FAMILY BACKGROUND, HIGH IDEALS

The dynamism and wealth of late nineteenth-century Cleveland contrasted with the privations and piety of John Lincoln's family background. He came from a family strongly rooted in Christian principles and the ideals of social reform. William Elleby Lincoln, father of John and James Lincoln, was British. During a cholera epidemic in 1855, William Lincoln heard one of Charles Grandison Finney's fire and brimstone sermons in Whitefield Chapel in London. The preacher was president of Oberlin College and pastor of Oberlin's First Congregational Church.[5] This encounter with American revivalism, with its determination to change the world for the better, altered the course of William Lincoln's life. He followed Finney back to Oberlin College where he began to study for the ministry. After joining the Abolitionist crusade, he took time off to travel and preach in the South against the evils of slavery. In 1858 he took part in the famous Oberlin-Wellington Rescue, organized to prevent an escaped slave from being returned to Kentucky under the infamous Fugitive Slave Law. This adventure landed Lincoln in the Cuyahoga County Jail in Cleveland, along with several other students, faculty members, and prominent citizens of Oberlin. Their incarceration, the subject of public demonstrations and widely read press accounts, made them martyrs to the Abolitionist cause. Upon release, the rescuers returned to Oberlin to a hero's welcome.[6]

Participation in the Oberlin-Wellington Rescue prolonged William Lincoln's years as a student, but it also brought an important steadying force into the impetuous Englishman's life. During the festivities to celebrate the rescuers' homecoming, a young Oberlin student first noticed the tall, clean-shaven twenty-seven-year-old. His future wife, Frances Louisa Marshall, came from a respectable Painesville family, long active in promoting education, particularly the education of women. Her mother, Roxanna Marshall, a strong supporter of women's suffrage, taught at the Lake Erie Female Seminary, now Lake Erie College.[7]

Back at Oberlin Seminary, Lincoln's outspokenness in matters of theology made him unpopular with the faculty. He brazenly incurred Finney's displeasure and "freely found fault & came into collision" with his successor, James Harris Fairchild.[8] His marriage to Louisa Marshall in 1865 sealed his fate. Because students of the ministry were forbidden to marry before graduation, he was refused a diploma.

Louisa offered her husband the stability and level-headed good sense that he seemed to lack. Nevertheless, the early years of their marriage tested her mettle. After William Lincoln's ordination in the Congregational Church in Hope, Ohio, near Columbus, the couple returned briefly to the Marshall family farm, where Louisa gave birth on July 17, 1866, to John Cromwell Lincoln, the first of ten children, only four of whom survived childhood. Shortly afterwards, the couple headed for Berea College in Kentucky to teach. There he received a salary of $50 a month and she, $30.

Teaching, however, failed to satisfy William's restless spirit. He responded to a call to serve as a missionary in the wilds of Northern Michigan where their second son, Paul Martyn Lincoln (named after a well-known British missionary to India), was born. In 1870 William assumed the pastorate of an affluent congregation in Marysville, Ohio. The young minister, however, had an unfortunate knack for picking sermon topics his parishioners were fond of, the better to attack them. A member of the Prohibition party, he inveighed against the evils of liquor. He also denounced Free Masonry, a popular fraternal order. Lincoln's Marysville parishioners resented his crusading spirit and unrestrained expression of controversial political views. They demanded his resignation.[9]

The family returned to Northeast Ohio to prepare for missionary work abroad. Louisa attended the Cleveland Homeopathic Hospital College, intending to minister to the sick while her husband served the spiritual needs of the converted. Although Louisa completed her degree in 1875, the Lincolns did not receive the hoped-for posting to the Far East. Though she never set up a medical practice, she continued throughout her life to see patients who called at her back door.

William Lincoln's reputation as a "feckless clergyman, always getting into bitter arguments with parishioners and being let out after a year or two of a pastorate" made steady income impossible.[10] During the next decade the family moved frequently, serving ever smaller congregations in Sinclairville, New York, and New Rutland, Prairie Home, and Blair, Illinois.

With the exception of one year of formal schooling in Marysville in the first grade, John Lincoln was educated by his mother at home, along with Paul (later Dean of the Engineering School at Cornell University) and his sister, Mary Grace, a future graduate of Lake Erie College. Too poor to afford school books, Louisa Lincoln provided her children with a solid grounding in the Bible.

In contrast to his father's brashness, John Lincoln was both reticent and soft-spoken, but the Oberlin-inspired perfectionism of his mother and father left its mark. John Lincoln rejected the idea of a kingdom of heaven, separate and above the work-a-day world. He believed that individuals had within themselves the ability and the duty to reform both themselves and society. In his seventies, he wrote an interpretation of the Gospels called *Christ's Object in Life*. In this short book, focused

If William Lincoln had spread the Gospel through preaching, John used his talents to invent things, establish companies, and put people to work.

on the first three books of the New Testament, he stressed that Christ's mission was to "establish a new and better society" on this earth.[11] "Can we do better than to catch part of the vision He had and use our lives to help rid the world of evils and the wars and poverty and broken lives that result from evil," he asked.[12] If William Lincoln had spread the Gospel through preaching, John used his talents to invent things, establish companies, and put people to work. He would also engage in an variety of philanthropic activities that reflected his activist interpretation of Christian teachings.

Upon the family's return to Ohio, William Lincoln became the minister of a small parish at Fairport Harbor, near the Marshall family farm in Painesville. On May 14, 1883, James Finney Lincoln was born. He was named after the charismatic preacher who had once figured so prominently in his father's spiritual life. Three years later the family moved to the Marshall farm so that Louisa could care for her aging mother. This was the first settled existence that John Lincoln had known.

During his three years at Painesville High School, John Lincoln's encounter with physics and a laboratory equipped with a single electric magneto opened up a strange and exciting new world. His teacher told him: "Some fool named Edison made a light with electricity a few years ago."[13] John set up a laboratory in a shed adjacent to the house and resolved to learn all he could about electricity. In 1884 he set out for Columbus for his final year of high school to learn Greek, at that time required for entrance to Ohio State University. Room and board in exchange for chores on a local Columbus farm made it possible for him to afford to live away from home.

When John Lincoln enrolled in Ohio State University the following year, it consisted of a small cluster of modest brick buildings surrounded by fields. Founded in 1873 as the Ohio Agricultural and Mechanical College, the institution offered courses in mechanical engineering for the first time in 1878. Lincoln wanted to study electrical engineering, but the university offered few courses in this new specialty. To continue his experiments, he set up a makeshift electrical laboratory in the house where he boarded. To gain practical experience he took a job with a Columbus traction company installing the city's first electric streetcar line. With little patience for degree requirements, he left Ohio State after three years for his first position with the Brush Electric

Company. Twenty-five years later, the university awarded him the honorary degree of Electrical Engineer in Mechanical Engineering retroactive to 1888.

Returning to Northeast Ohio, Lincoln took a job in the training program at the Brush Electric Company in Cleveland, where he earned ten cents an hour. This was good money and a foot in the door of a company that could provide him with valuable training. In the mid-1880s the Brush Electric Company offered a practical introduction to young men with a flair for engineering. After hands-on experience on the factory floor assembling arc lamps and testing dynamos, Lincoln accepted a job with one of Brush's associates, Sidney Howe Short, a graduate of Ohio State and a pioneer in the electric-railway industry.[14] This work took Lincoln to Muskegon, Michigan; Indianapolis, Indiana; Columbus and Cincinnati, Ohio; Pittsburgh, Pennsylvania; Covington, Kentucky; and Parkersburg, West Virginia, to install Short's electric street-railway systems. In 1891 Lincoln supervised the installation of an entire system consisting of seventy cars for the city of Rochester, New York. In his spare time he invented a regenerative control system that adapted the car's drive motor to function as a dynamo, with the load serving as a brake to slow the car. This concept, known as dynamic braking, is still in use today in many applications, including locomotives. Lincoln sold the rights to this patent to Elmer Ambrose Sperry, another Cleveland inventor who dreamed of designing an urban electric railway system. Sperry later would move on to Minneapolis to found the Sperry Gyroscope Company, progenitor of the Unisys Corporation.[15] During this period, Lincoln also tinkered with a motor with better torque characteristics to power elevators. His other patents in the electrical field included an electric drill, an apparatus for curing meat, an electrically controlled mine door opener, and an arc light.

The association of the Elliott brothers with an engineer of Lincoln's mechanical ingenuity and experience offered them new opportunities for expanding their business.

In 1892 Lincoln returned to Cleveland to take charge of construction for Short's street railway company. A year later Short fired him, blaming Lincoln for the failure of a motor manufactured by the Brush Electric Company. Lincoln then cast his lot with Emmett Elliott and his two brothers, W. H. and Samuel K., who owned a small electrical

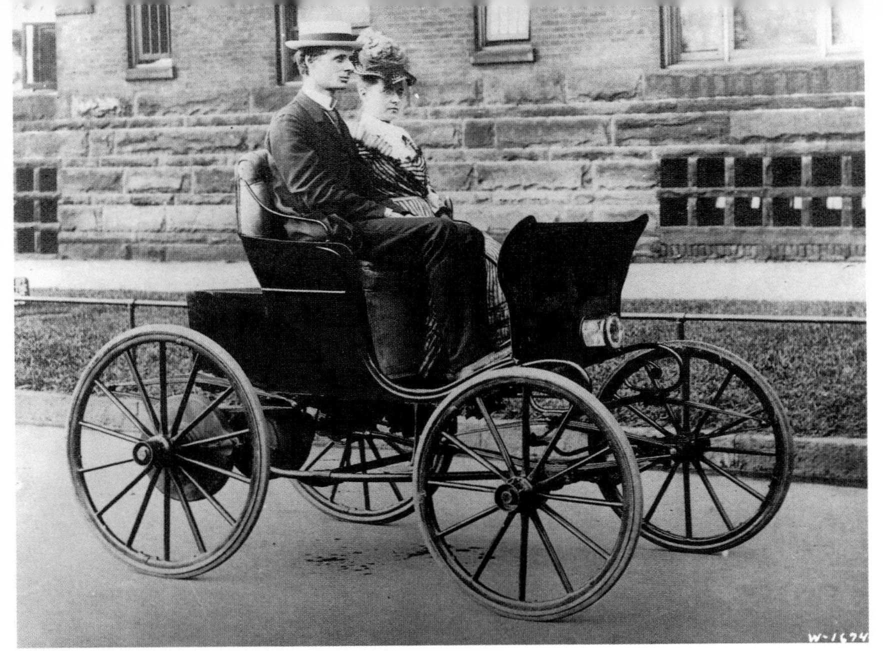

John C. Lincoln and his wife ride in a vehicle with the dynamo-motor he designed in 1900 during the heyday of the electric car.

repair shop adjacent to the Pennsylvania Railroad right-of-way near Carnegie Avenue. He had met Emmett Elliott four years earlier in Brush's training program. The association of the Elliott brothers with an engineer of Lincoln's mechanical ingenuity and experience offered them new opportunities for expanding their business. For the Elliotts, Lincoln designed a small electric motor that he described as "not nearly so good as it might have been, but it was better than many on the market."[16] When sales appeared promising, they rewarded him by making him president of the company, renamed the Elliott-Lincoln Electric Company in 1894. Electric motors that could be adapted to a variety of uses, particularly in machine shops like that of the Elliott brothers, found a niche in the market.

Success proved fleeting. When the company began to founder, the Elliotts forced Lincoln out – into the spare bedroom of his Marcy Avenue home (now East 86th Street). On Marcy Avenue, with wife and children underfoot, he filled custom orders for electric motors and continued to tinker with new inventions. His lucky break came when Herbert Henry Dow, a Case Institute of Technology graduate and future head of the Dow Chemical Corporation, asked him to redesign a motor for a cement mill. John Lincoln used the $250 fee for this motor as capital for The Lincoln Electric Company.[17] He launched this future *Fortune* 500 corporation in December 1895 "with more nerve than knowledge" in the midst of a severe recession. To a minister's son who had experienced the privations of an itinerant childhood, motors provided the promise of a stable and prosperous future.

Between 1885 and 1890, developments in alternating current equipment, particularly the transformers and generators sold by Westinghouse and somewhat later by General Electric, as well as Nicola Tesla's polyphase electric motor, initiated the shift to electricity by industries previously powered by steam. However, only after the turn of the century, with the growth of the electric utility industry and especially the availability of cheap electricity supplied by central stations in urban areas, did electrification of industry occur on a large scale.[18]

Lincoln's plan was to improve upon the electric motor he had designed for the Elliotts. He aimed to make his new direct-current motor as simple, durable, and inexpensive as possible. That same year, he took out a second patent on his motor and opened his own shop in the Perkins Power

Block in downtown Cleveland. Several weeks later he moved to the fourth floor of a building at the corner of St. Clair Avenue and Ontario Street. Lincoln did a brisk business selling his motors to small manufacturing concerns, machine shops, and elevator companies. A year later he began to manufacture motor-generator sets to serve as low-voltage dynamos. After a fire ruined his small operation, he set up shop on the third floor of the World Building at 71 and 73 Ontario Street.[19]

No task seemed too small or too daunting. He filled custom orders for motors and still found time to produce a popular handbook on electricity called *Practical Electricity with Questions and Answers*. First published as a series of lectures by the Cleveland Armature Works in 1896, it sold 40,000 copies. The book was simple and straightforward. Lincoln discussed the state of the art shortly before the turn of the century. He began with wiring and moved through discussions of batteries, magnetic traction, winding of dynamos and motors, and "diseases of dynamos and motors, their symptoms and how to cure them." The final chapter tackled the subject of electric automobiles, then briefly in their heyday in Cleveland.[20]

Lincoln put theory into practice. He built his own battery-powered vehicle in 1900. On flat terrain it could reach a top speed of about 16 miles an hour. It was equipped with batteries manufactured by the Willard Storage Battery Company, another Cleveland company whose founders had

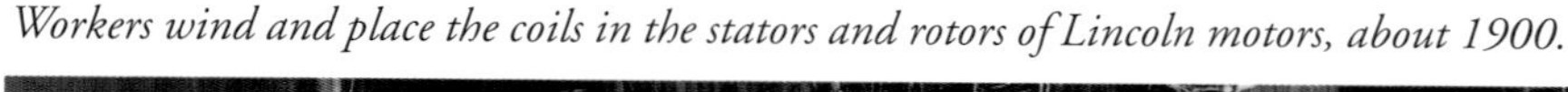

Workers wind and place the coils in the stators and rotors of Lincoln motors, about 1900.

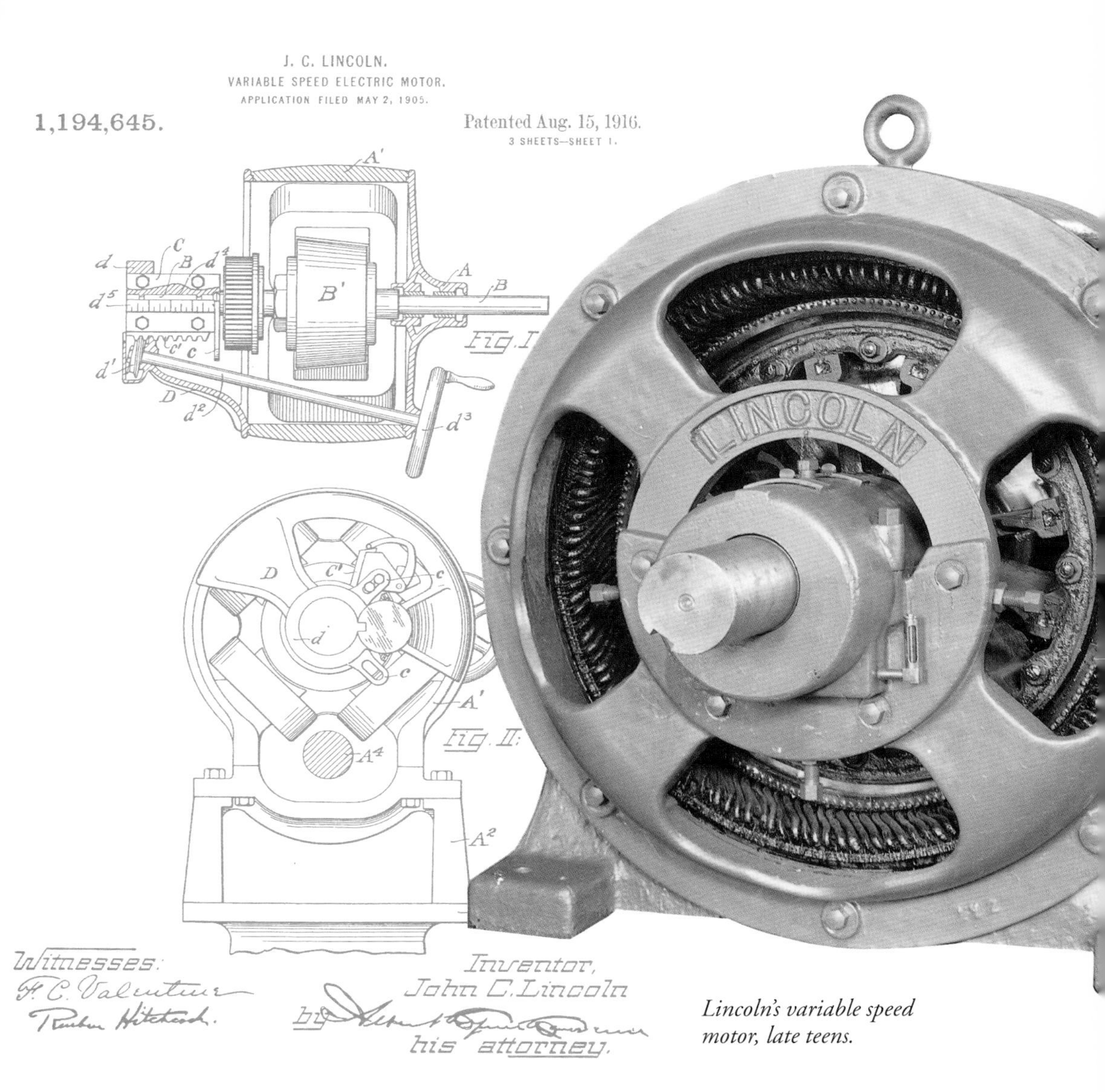

Lincoln's variable speed motor, late teens.

close personal ties with Lincoln. The dynamo-motor he designed for his automobile was light, as well as capable of operating at variable speeds.[21] He applied for a patent for the ingenious variable-speed electric motor. He considered this motor his greatest invention. The design avoided the sparking at the point where the brushes met the commutator, characteristic of other motors of this type. "It has been my purpose," he wrote, "to accomplish these results by the simplest practicable means and without the reduction of efficiency in the motor as modified by my improvements." [22] About this time Lincoln began to sell motor-generator sets for use as battery chargers for electric automobiles. The Lincoln motor-generator sets enabled automobile owners to charge their batteries overnight in their own garages or at a service station.

In 1906 Lincoln incorporated The Lincoln Electric Company with a capitalization of $10,000 divided into 100 shares of $100 each. He bought land from his old employer, Charles Brush, and erected his first factory on Kelley Avenue and East 38th Street at a cost of between $20,000 and $25,000. Although forced to pay his workers for several months with scrip during the 1907 panic, the move took place as planned the following year. At the new location, he was able to expand his work force to thirty and his business began to earn between $50,000 and $60,000 per year.[23]

The potential market for Lincoln's direct-current motors appealed to Lincoln's cousins, Ruben and Charles Hitchcock. They convinced their father Peter Hitchcock in 1904 to form a partnership with Lincoln to market his patented adjustable-speed armature-shifting DC motor. This venture, incorporated as the Lincoln Motor Works in 1907 became the Reliance Electric & Engineering Company. After Lincoln sold his interest in the company for $25,000, Reliance Electric continued to specialize in adjustable-speed direct-current motors.

THE POLITICS OF REFORM

During the years he had worked for Brush Electric, John Lincoln heard the economist Henry George lecture on his single-tax theory. He admitted that at that time he "had no idea what George was talking about."[24] But the dawn of the new century – a time when Lincoln was struggling to build Lincoln Electric – produced a quickening of Lincoln's interest in and eventual conversion to George's radical economic philosophy. Like George, Lincoln believed that the elimination of all taxes on industry, personal property, buildings, and improvements would free the enterprising individual to focus on creating a profitable business.

George's single-tax theory offered a solution to the economic evils of capitalism, while preserving its basic structure. George did not advocate doing away with private ownership of land, but he wanted to make taxes on land so high that they would discourage land speculation. Land served as the base for the "industrial pyramid." Without access to land, capital and labor could not create wealth for society. George regarded land speculators as society's drones. They accumulated great personal wealth without any exertion at all – simply by holding land. George thought land should be taxed according to its value to the community. To force all needed land into use, heavily urbanized areas with a high concentration of population should bear the highest taxes. But the government should refrain from taxing improvements on the land. High taxes on the producers of society, such as inventor-entrepreneurs, store owners, and industrious farmers, robbed them of incentive. The community ought to leave to the "individual producer all that prompts him to exertion."[25] The more that labor and capital together produced, the greater the general wealth of the society.

George and his followers believed that the increasing chasm between rich and poor had caused the social and economic problems that plagued the end of the nineteenth century.

With the land speculator gone, the entrepreneur and his employees could effectively work together for their mutual benefit. Their enterprise would create jobs.

George and his followers believed that the increasing chasm between rich and poor had caused the social and economic problems that plagued the end of the nineteenth century. The great material progress of the nineteenth century, symbolized by the steam engine, the railroads, and the telegraph, had created great wealth for the privileged few and grinding poverty for multitudes of helpless people. "It is as though an immense wedge were being forced," George wrote in *Progress and Poverty*, "not underneath society, but through society. Those who are above the point of separation are elevated, but those who are below are crushed down."[26] Industrial depressions wreaked havoc on small businesses like Lincoln Electric and caused widespread unemployment. George believed that land and the rights to the natural resources that went along with ownership, was a commodity to be accumulated and exploited for private gain. Imagining the earth as a ship well provided with supplies for its journey through space, he described the imbalance of power created by ownership of natural resources: "It is a well provisioned ship, this on which we sail through space. If the bread and beef above decks seem to grow scarce, we open a hatch and there is a new supply, of which before we never dreamed. And very great command over the services of others comes to those who as the hatches are opened are permitted to say, 'This is mine.'"[27]

Lincoln's conversion to George's single-tax theory occurred during Cleveland's progressive years after Tom Johnson became mayor in 1901. Johnson cleaned house, ridding the city of the corrupt Republican machine politicians, many of whom had owed allegiance to Mark L. Hanna, Johnson's former adversary in the street-railway business. Johnson's monopolies in the steel business and in street-railway systems had made him a millionaire, but after reading Henry George's *Social Problems*, he saw the error of his ways. The power of George's ideas influenced Johnson to sell his businesses and run for public office – four times for United States Congressman. He won two terms in 1890 and 1892 with George acting as his mentor and closest advisor. He served as mayor of the City of Cleveland between 1901 and 1909.

Henry George's ideas became the basis of Johnson's new creed of economic fairness and responsible government. Johnson attacked the practice of granting franchises for public utilities to individuals with political clout. Monopolies of electric utilities, railroad rights-of-way, and franchises for street-railway systems granted by corrupt city officials often led to artificially high rate structures. The public that depended on these basic services suffered while a privileged few individuals enriched themselves. "My ambition," he told journalist Lincoln Steffens, "is to make Cleveland the first American city to get good government."[28]

Johnson did not think that implementation of the single tax was an impossibly utopian notion; he saw it as a just and necessary objective. Although he failed to achieve the goal of a single tax during his tenure as mayor, he was able to bring about a reassessment of property values in the city so that there was no longer a tax advantage to holding undeveloped land for speculation. He eloquently summarized the benefits of a single tax to society in his autobiography, *My Story*. "Any man competent to do business could find profitable business to do because the effective demand for goods would always exceed the output. There could be no oppressive organization of capital, because capital would have no privileges. There could be no coercive labor unions because every worker would be his own all-sufficient union. And there would be no tyrannical government because all the people would be economically free, a condition that makes tyranny, either economic or political, impossible."[29] Although there is no documentation to illuminate the nature of John Lincoln's relationship with Mayor Johnson, they shared the same enthusiasm for George's theories. Lincoln's advocacy of the single tax gave his life a new purpose, reinforced his strong Christian beliefs, and ultimately led him to give up active management of Lincoln Electric – but not before he took steps to ensure that Lincoln Electric would continue to thrive under the leadership of his capable, much-younger brother.

CREATING A FAMILY BUSINESS

In 1907 when John Lincoln offered a job to James Finney Lincoln he could not have foreseen the impact that the young man would have on the future of the company. Growing up 17 years apart, the two brothers represented different generations of entrepreneurs. John Lincoln had come of age in the heyday of inventor-entrepreneurs like Charles Brush. James Finney Lincoln had more in common with industrialists like Henry Ford. He had Ford's organizational skills and shared his enthusiasm for mass production. Unlike John's unsettled childhood, James grew up in Painesville, Ohio, on the Marshall family farm. Always an avid sportsman, his quarry from the woods outside the town and fish from the Grand River often provided welcome sustenance for the family. James

Lincoln motors installed in a West Virginia pulp and paper mill, about 1915.

matured into a gregarious young man – his personality more like that of the fiery preacher, after whom he was named, than his quiet, unassuming older brother. Upon graduation from Painesville High School in 1901, he entered Ohio State University where by 1903 there was a bona fide electrical engineering program. He had paid his tuition with savings from a $74-a-year janitorial job in the schoolhouse and church, and a timely loan from brother John.

Robust, handsome, and aggressive, J.F. Lincoln loved football, and the game shaped his ideas about what motivated people to excel. A star fullback and defensive stalwart, he had served as the team's captain during the 1906 season when no opposing team crossed Ohio State's goal. Lincoln's tactic was the "flying wedge." Ohio State's small quarterback would grab hold of fullback Lincoln's belt. "Captain-Fullback Lincoln would become the eye of the storm, the center of that wedge," a teammate recalled. "Behind him, the entire Buckeye team would surge forward to flay the foe."[30] After a bout with typhoid fever prevented him from graduating with his class, Lincoln took a job at Union Carbide with his brother Paul in Niagara Falls for a short time. In 1907 when he accepted John's offer of a position in sales with Lincoln Electric, he agreed to a salary of $50 per month plus a commission of 2 percent of sales. The next year, after he married Alice Josephine Patterson of Cleveland, he requested a salary of $150 a month and a commission of 1 percent of sales, an agreement that continued in effect throughout his career at Lincoln Electric.

James Lincoln's early years at Lincoln Electric were spent in the field calling on prospects while John managed the factory. It appears that the company was managed more by the seat of the pants than rational plan. About 1910 a report prepared by a management consultant observed, "In making our investigation, we find several conditions which are not only incorrect from a business standpoint, but which would cause you considerable trouble and loss of money as the business continues." The consultant called the company's accounting procedures crude. "You do not have any control of your material or labor," he chided, "and no attempt is made to regulate in proportion to the volume of business."[31]

Early welding equipment with wall-mounted control panel, undated.

Motors were the mainstay of the company at this time.[32] Lincoln Electric motors had a range of industrial applications. Early advertising pictured Lincoln motors running large lithographing presses, sewing machine line shafts, linotype machines, air compressors at a meat curing factory, blowers for a stove company, and picker and carding machinery at a mattress company. Lincoln motors were rugged. They performed well under grueling conditions where moisture and dirt damaged ordinary motors. Sales literature pictured a motor that had continued to operate for more than two years submerged in a water tank.

In the electric motor field The Lincoln Electric Company had to compete with larger, more diversified companies, like General Electric and Westinghouse. Unlike competitors, the company insisted on strict adherence to published prices and did not give a price break for quantity orders. "One price for all" was a cardinal rule. The company touted its motors as more durable than those of its "name plate" competitors and was willing to back this up by actual on-site tests. Lincoln motors could take a 25 percent overload for long periods, while comparable motors made by competitors could take overloads for only short periods. The difference could be attributed to 15 percent more material for the same rating and the employment of skilled labor in its factory. "This is in direct opposition to the custom of at least one of the larger manufacturers who do the majority of their stock machine winding by girls working piece work, insuring the most rapid and most careless job which can be accomplished."[33] This view of piecework would change under the inspiration of scientific management introduced by James Lincoln.

Exactly when and how The Lincoln Electric Company became involved in welding is unclear. A typescript in the company archives traces J. C. Lincoln's interest to 1907 when he built his first welding equipment for brazing copper bonds to streetcar rails.[34] John C. Lincoln's biographer places his interest in arc welding somewhat later.[35] It may be no coincidence that he began his experiments in arc welding about the time a challenge of a German arc welding patent may have opened up the field.[36]

J. F. Lincoln also mentioned 1907 as the date the company began to experiment with fabricating arc welding equipment. He recalled that one of his early customers at the Steel Castings Company in Cleveland told him that what the steel industry needed was a method to fix broken castings. At this time Cleveland's location as one of the major Great Lakes ports had made it a center of the American iron and steel industry. Iron, shipped in the hulls of ore boats owned by Cleveland Cliffs and Pickands Mather, was processed into steel in Cleveland. U. S. Steel had wire and strip mills on the Ohio and Erie Canal. Blast furnaces of the Corrigan-McKinney Steel Company hugged the east bank of the Cuyahoga River. The Cleveland Rolling Mill, along with the Otis Iron and Steel Company, were also located in the Flats along the river. These mills apparently used huge stationary transformer-type arc welding units, operated simultaneously by several men, to make repairs on defective iron and steel castings. According to J. F. Lincoln, one of the problems was the difficulty of holding a steady arc.[37] Presumably, John Lincoln responded to this need by developing a "variable voltage machine," favorably reviewed in a trade publication in 1911. The Lincoln Arc Welder was lighter and consumed far less electricity than competitors' machines. Most importantly, a large current-resisting stabilizer, through which the output of current could be adjusted, allowed the operator to control the intensity of the arc. "By use of this welder, the length of the arc determines entirely the amount of current flowing and by varying the length of the arc the amount of current which is flowing can be automatically varied." The Lincoln Arc Welder came equipped with an ammeter, main switch, arc switch, and field regulator. The control board could be mounted

Exactly when and how the Lincoln Electric Company became involved in welding is unclear.

The Lincoln Electric Company's work force, 1910. John Lincoln is in center.

on an adjacent wall or on the machine itself. Mounting the controls directly on the motor-generator set and placing it on a sturdy metal wagon made it portable, though at 1,500 pounds moving the Lincoln Arc Welder must have been an arduous process.[38]

Early sales literature directed at the "leading steel foundrymen of the world" pointed out that the Lincoln Arc Welder could correct blowholes, shrinkage cracks and misruns, saving about 90 percent of the foundry's steel castings from the scrap heap. The arc welder could be shut down when not in use. Arc welding also could be used in plants and machine shops for repairs of gray iron and malleable castings. The company took responsibility for every detail of installation. At no extra charge within 500 miles of Cleveland, it sent out an "experienced electrician" with each machine to make the necessary electrical connections and to instruct the operator, remaining with him "until he can secure perfect results."[39]

Despite the future potential of arc welding, it is unlikely that young Jim Lincoln – master salesman that he was – sold many welding units before the 1920s. The Lincoln Arc Welder (a motor-generator set like the Lincoln battery charger) became one of the company's standard products after demand for electric cars declined about 1917. In the meantime, in 1913 the death of John Lincoln's invalid wife precipitated a nervous breakdown. John left James in charge of the company and set off for a trip through Europe where he visited some of the leading proponents of Henry George's economic theories. Upon his return the following year, John named brother James vice president and general manager. Although John continued as president and principal stockholder, he never again assumed active management.

Like Edison and other creative inventor-entrepreneurs of his generation, John Lincoln chose to turn over day-to-day management to people more gifted in directing the work of others. In his workshop-laboratory at 2400 Woodland Avenue he continued his experiments to improve arc welding processes, motors, and dynamos. One of the more challenging technical problems he tackled was how to prevent welded metals from becoming brittle and breaking at or adjacent to the welded seam. In 1914 he patented his idea of applying finely powdered metals, such as magnesium, aluminum, copper, manganese, or zinc, adjacent to the edges or surfaces of steel sheets to be joined. The heat of the arc melted the metals into an alloy to produce a weld that was both strong and ductile.[40] The idea of using a flux to enhance the welding process became the basis of his invention of the "Electronic Tornado," one of the first commercial processes for automatic welding. In 1928 he patented a welding process that used an inert gas, such as nitrogen or carbon dioxide, as a protective medium for the weld. The gas shield prevented oxidation and produced a strong, even weld.[41] Others, however, would develop the gas-shielded arc welding process to the dominant position it holds in the industry today.

John Lincoln's career as an entrepreneur continued after he gave up active management of The Lincoln Electric Company. In 1915 he formed a new company, the Electric Railway & Bonding Company, to capitalize on his patent for a new method of bonding rail-ends together, an aspect of his renewed interest in electric railways. He continued as president until 1920. With Jacob Kronheim, owner of a

The fabrication of a boiler using the Electric Tornado, 1922.

small shop on one of Lincoln's properties, he organized the Universal Wire Spring Company to capitalize on the development of zigzag, or corrugated springs, to replace coiled springs in automobile seats. Collaboration with Harold Neely resulted in the invention of an ingenious machine to manufacture these springs. It supplied Jeep seats during World War II, and following the war it became a major supplier to General Motors and furniture manufacturers.

John Lincoln continued to advocate George's single-tax theory as the means to the fair distribution of wealth and the economic well-being of the nation. In an effort to win a wider following for George's single tax, in 1924 he ran for vice president of the United States on the Commonwealth Land Party ticket. In 1931, at the age of 65, he moved to Phoenix, Arizona. He found the climate of the Southwest and a diet that included goat's milk reinforced his health and helped to soothe his wife's arthritis. Through the 1930s Lincoln continued to buy real estate in Ohio and Arizona at Depression prices. He purchased a large tract of land near Scottsdale and financed the development of the Camelback Inn, now an enormously popular resort.

The simplicity and modesty of the founder of Lincoln Electric became legendary within the company.

The spectacular appreciation of the value of the land he purchased during the Depression proved to Lincoln the validity of George's theories. This appreciation had occurred because society had added new value to the land. The community, not the landowner, had the moral right to collect ground rent in the form of taxes, thus freeing the government from dependence on the taxation of the earned income of its citizens.[42] Lincoln liberally supported the Henry George School of Social Science in New York City and served as president of the school for many years. With his real estate profits and a large block of stock in the Lincoln Electric Company, Lincoln created an endowment for The Lincoln Foundation in 1947 for the promotion of George's ideas. He saw George's theories as the antidote for the spread of communism. In *Christ's Object in Life*, a book that expressed John Lincoln's strong belief in the connection between the unjust distribution of wealth and social upheavals, he wrote:

> Sixty years ago, Henry George discovered a command of the Creator that is not generally known, and set it forth in his book "Progress and Poverty." That command could be stated, "Thou shalt not have a system of land distribution that results in unemployment and poverty and depressions and the unjust distribution of wealth." If anyone with understanding will read this book, they will be convinced that many of the social evils which bring war and communism and fascism are the penalties for breaking this commandment.[43]

John Lincoln in his later years at Camelback Inn near Scottsdale, Arizona.

Lincoln returned frequently to Cleveland with his third wife, Helen, to attend board meetings of The Lincoln Electric Company, look after his Ohio real estate, and visit family. Between 1951 and 1959 they summered in Cleveland with frequent weekend trips to Chautauqua Lake. When in Cleveland the Lincolns would stay at Wade Park Manor, a fashionable residential hotel. On one train trip from Phoenix, Lincoln came east alone. He reportedly put his shoes out for the Pullman porter to shine. On arriving in downtown Cleveland the next morning his shoes were nowhere to be found. Undeterred, he descended from the train in rumpled seersucker suit, straw hat and stocking feet. After the streetcar ride to University Circle he walked into the Wade Park Manor, where he was met with the icy glare of the manager. Lincoln politely dissuaded him from throwing him out. He explained, somewhat apologetically, that, as a matter of fact, he owned the Manor!

The simplicity and modesty of the founder of Lincoln Electric became legendary within the company. Former Lincoln employees from the 1930s recalled that he preferred public transportation. During his Cleveland visits, he seldom sat behind a desk provided for him in J. F. Lincoln's office, preferring to roam the factory floor to offer help with the solution of technical problems. A family member recalled he loved the stimulation of a good argument. He would twirl a half-open pen knife between his fingers, looking for some of his favorite employees. When he spotted one, he would walk up, state a proposition for the argument and ask whether his adversary wanted to argue for or against. The rules settled, they would carry on for a few minutes until one side had clearly prevailed or Lincoln had enough of the sport.

When John Lincoln died in 1959 in Scottsdale, Arizona, at the age of 92, he left an estate estimated at between $50 million and $100 million. His real estate holdings in Cleveland included the Wade Park Manor, Moreland Courts (exclusive apartment buildings on Shaker Square), and the Auditorium Hotel (built directly opposite the Public Auditorium on East 6th Street) and the Lincoln Building in downtown Cleveland. He also owned the Flamingo Hotel in Miami Beach, Florida, and the LeVeque-Lincoln Tower Building in Columbus, Ohio, at that time one of the largest office buildings in Ohio. His estate in Arizona included the Bagdad Copper Company, acquired in 1944, and Camelback Inn.[44]

Beyond these and other ventures, the enduring monument to John C. Lincoln's genius as an inventor-entrepreneur during this intensely creative period of Cleveland's industrial history is The Lincoln Electric Company. John remained president of Lincoln Electric until 1928, when he became chairman of the board of directors. In 1940 he began a program of giving stock to J. F. Lincoln and his family in an effort to make the holdings of each family roughly equal.[45]

Though John Lincoln remained actively involved in the company to the end of his life, he had the good sense to realize that to grow, American companies of the 1920s required people with both the vision to create a market for their products and the skills to manage people. By turning over the management of his company to his brother in 1913, John Lincoln assured the company's future. His sense of mission – the commitment to values that transcended the work-a-day world – would live on in the incentive philosophy of James Finney Lincoln. J. F. Lincoln would prove himself equally capable in shaping the field of arc welding and in laying down the principles of management that still infuse the company's culture.

---

[1] A. Michal McMahon, *The Making of a Profession: A Century of Electrical Engineering in America* (New York: Institute of Electrical and Electronics Engineering Press, 1984), 17-24.

[2] On Brush see, Howard K. Passer, *The Electrical Manufacturers 1875-1900* (Cambridge: Harvard University Press, 1953) and Harry J. Eisenman, III, "Charles F. Brush: Pioneer Innovator in Electrical Technology," Ph.D. Dissertation, Case Institute of Technology, 1967.

[3] "The 'Brush' Factory at Cleveland," *Electrical World*, Aug. 1, 1885. 43.

[4] Although poorly organized, sometimes inaccurate, and without an index, R. D. Simonson, *The History of Welding* (Morton Grove, IL: Monticello Books, 1969) contains much historical material unavailable elsewhere. For an early bibliography of welding, see William B. Gamble, compiler, "List of Works Relating to Electric Welding," *Bulletin of the New York Public Library* 17 (1913): 375-393. Also, Howard B. Cary, *Modern Welding Technology*, 2nd ed. (Englewood Cliffs: Prentice Hall, 1989), 5-10. A. C. Nunes, Jr., "Gas Welding Origins," *Welding Journal* 56(1977): 15-23; "Arc Welding Origins," *Welding Journal* 55(1976): 566-572.

[5] Raymond Moley, *The American Century of John C. Lincoln* (N.Y.: Duell, Sloan and Pierce, 1962), 9.

[6] On the Oberlin-Wellington Rescue, see Nat Brandt, T*he Town that Started the Civil War* (Syracuse: Syracuse University Press, 1990), and Jacob R. Shipherd, *History of the Oberlin-Wellington Rescue* (Boston: J. Paul Jewett & Company,1859). On William Lincoln, see also William E. Lincoln to Gerrit Smith, July 5, 1859, April 20, 1861, Fletcher Papers. Response to letter from Philip D. Sherman, March 1918, to Mrs. William E. Lincoln, dated March 1918, written on the back of Sherman's letter. Secretary's Office, 1833-1970, Oberlin College Archives, Oberlin, Ohio.

[7] On Frances Louisa Lincoln and the Lincoln family, see Frank D. Newbury, "The Lincoln Family Genealogy" typescript [1958].

[8] Raymond Moley, 15.

[9] Raymond Moley, 19.

[10] See John W. Love to Secretary [Donald Love], Oberlin College, September 13, 1956, Alumni Records [Formers/Graduates] 1933-1960], William E. Lincoln, Oberlin College Archives.

[11] Raymond Moley, 144.

[12] Raymond Moley, 152.

[13] Oren Arnold, "Electric Lincolns," *The Lion*, Feb. 1955, 8-10.

[14] For biographical material on Short, see S. Winifred Smith, "Sidney Howe Short," *Museum Echoes* 28 (1955):75-6 and Raymond Moley, 33-34, 37-38.

[15] On Sperry see Raymond Moley, 37, and Thomas Park Hughes, *Elmer Sperry: Inventor and Engineer* (Baltimore: The Johns Hopkins University Press, 1971).

[16] Raymond Moley, 39.

[17] Frank D. Newbury, 14.

[18] See Richard B. Du Boff, "The Introduction of Electric Power in American Manufacturing," *Economic History Review* 20 (1967): 509-518. Raymond Moley, 58 ff.

[19] Raymond Moley, 58 ff.

[20] [John C. Lincoln], *Practical Electricity with Questions and Answers* (Cleveland: A. C. Rogers Co., 4th ed., 1904).

[21] See"An Efficient Type of Motor,"*Motor Age*, Sept. 6, 1900.

[22] "Variable-speed electric motor," U.S. Patent #829,975, Sept. 4, 1906. See also, letter from James Lincoln to Dr. E. E. Dreese, Ohio State University, April 17, 1939. LEC archives.

[23] Raymond Moley, 64-5. Copies of the Articles of Incorporation, 1906, and certificates of increase of capital stock of 1911, 1913, 1914, 1919 and 1965 can be found in the LEC archives.

[24] Raymond Moley, 161.

[25] Henry George, *Progress and Poverty* (N.Y.: Modern Library, 1938), 436.

[26] Henry George, 9.

[27] Henry George, 243.

[28] Lincoln Steffens, "Ohio: A Tale of Two Cities," *McClure's Magazine*, 25 (July, 1905): 302. See also Hoyt Landon Warner, *Progressivism in Ohio, 1897-1917* (Columbus: Ohio State University Press, 1964), 54-86.

[29] Tom L. Johnson, *My Story* (Kent, OH: Kent State University Press, repr. 1911 edition, 1993), 154-55.

[30] Jack Fullen, "Jim Lincoln Leaves a Legend," *Ohio State University Monthly*, July 1965, 4.

[31] Fragment of a report prepared by Miller, Franklin & Stevenson, about 1909-1911. LEC archives.

[32] Motors remained part of the product mix until World War II when motor production was halted. Motors were reintroduced in 1955. In 1965 Neal Manross improved the Lincoln motor through the introduction of the extruded aluminum frame and automatic winding of stator coils.

[33] "Sample Installations of Lincoln Machinery Installed in Cleveland," January 1912, Lincoln Electric Company, LEC archives.

[34] Typescript, "Biographical Sketch of Mr. John Cromwell Lincoln," March 25, 1937. LEC archives.

[35] Raymond Moley, 68.

[36] R. D. Simonson, 23-24.

[37] "Mr. Lincoln's Formula," *Fortune*, February 1944, reprint. LEC archives.

[38] "An Electric Arc Welder," *Iron Trade Review*, Aug. 10, 1911, 245-46. On the Cleveland iron and steel industry, see Carol Poh Miller's article in *The Encyclopedia of Cleveland History*, 578-581.

[39] "The Lincoln Arc Welder" pamphlet [no date], LEC archives.

[40] "Process of Welding Metals," U.S. Patent #1,108,592, Aug. 25, 1914.

[41] "Method and Means for Electric Arc Welding," U.S. Patent # 1,521,894, Jan. 6, 1925; "Method of Electric Arc Welding," U.S. Patent #1,711,151, April 30, 1929.

[42] "The Lincoln Foundation, founded by John C. Lincoln in 1947," brochure, 1958, The Hagley Library Archives, Wilmington, Delaware. See also Raymond Moley, 112.

[43] John C. Lincoln, *Christ's Object in Life* (Pacific Printing Co., 1948), 44. See also H. James Brown, *Land Use & Taxation* (Cambridge MA: Lincoln Institute of Land Policy, 1997).

[44] Obituary of John C. Lincoln, Plain Dealer, May 26, 1959.

[45] J. C. Lincoln to Frank Snell, June 17, 1940, papers of Harry Carlson.

"Successful management," declared James F. Lincoln, "...requires the intelligence of a genius, the patience of a Job, the fighting ability of a Spartan, and the enthusiasm of a nut."

Chapter 2

J.F. Lincoln Takes Charge, 1914-1929

In 1914, when Lincoln took over as general manager of The Lincoln Electric Company, he was just thirty-one. He stripped off his coat, rolled up his sleeves and went out on the factory floor to "get the hang of things" from the people in the factory. A reporter for the *Railway Workers Journal*, looking back on Lincoln's early years as manager, described him as a young man who had the confidence of a skilled athlete, a certain steely determination, and a way with people. Lincoln told him: "I knew that if I could get the people of the company to want the company to succeed as badly as I did, there would be no problems we could not solve together."[1] This attitude would shape his approach to management throughout his career. J. F. Lincoln did not underestimate the importance of face-to-face contact with his workers. He was often seen in shirt-sleeves on the factory floor. A key element in the success of his management system was his day-to-day involvement in all aspects of running the company.

At the end of World War I, Lincoln realized the work force he had required for meeting wartime demands was far greater than he would need for peacetime production, but he resisted laying people off. Shirkers he dismissed, but he wanted to retain workers who had demonstrated initiative and commitment to their work. Rather than reduce wages, he urged his staff to find ways to increase efficiency.[2] That year he was able to declare the company's first dividend and he paid his workers a small bonus of about 3 percent of wages for the year. The unenthusiastic response of his workers to this token caused Lincoln to abandon the bonus the following year. Years later, during the Great Depression, he would try the bonus idea again with far different results.

In 1923 the company moved into a plant on Coit Road, abandoned by the bankrupt Grant Motor Car Company.

Post-World War I Cleveland was the fifth largest city in the United States – a metropolis begrimed with the soot and smog of hundreds of factories, its prosperity fueled by the aspirations of first- and second-generation European immigrants. In 1923, as the company began to grow, Lincoln moved operations to the Collinwood neighborhood. The factory, located on Coit Road in a building abandoned by the bankrupt Grant Motor Car Company, remained the home of Lincoln Electric until it moved to nearby Euclid in 1951. The vast railroad yards of the Lake Shore & Michigan Southern Railroad (later New York Central) had paved the way for the economic and industrial development of the area, known as "Slovenian Heights" because of its concentration of Slovenians, Croatians, and Lithuanians. The neighborhood provided laborers skilled in a variety of trades, the backbone of Cleveland's expanding industrial base.

In 1925 the company introduced its "Linc-Weld" motor, featuring a design that replaced the cast-iron frame of conventional electric motors with rolled-steel "Linc-Welded" into a single piece.

J. F. Lincoln abandoned his brother's practice of building custom motors for Lincoln Electric's customers. Before the war, as the company's first, and for a time, only salesman, he had often returned to the factory to discover to his dismay that the company was no longer making the motor he had just sold. Lincoln credited the rapid growth of the company from near bankruptcy in 1913 to "the picking of two main lines of work and discarding of everything else."[3] Westinghouse and General Electric, the company's main competitors in the motor business, manufactured scores of products. In Lincoln's view, the effort to develop different types of products increased overhead and resulted in lower output per man. It also made it more difficult to respond quickly to customer needs. The only possible advantage to diversification lay in creating name recognition. Lincoln preferred to stake the company's reputation on a quality product and trained sales engineers. In 1925 the company introduced its "Linc-Weld" motor, featuring a design that replaced the cast-iron frame of conventional electric motors with rolled-steel "Linc-Welded" into a single piece. An advertisement in the *Saturday Evening Post* claimed, "For the first time, steel actually replaces cast iron in the making of electric motors – and with amazing results!"[4] Welded steel made the motor "practically unbreakable,"

lighter and easier to maintain. In addition to a welded frame, fourteen welded points within the motor contributed to improvements in the rotor, the oiling system, and the laminations.

Lincoln's most important decision was to sharpen the focus of the company on arc welding. In 1915 the company had introduced a new improved "variable voltage" welder on wheels.[5] The superior arc characteristics of this welding machine represented a significant advance over the relatively heavy and expensive welder the company had sold since 1911. In 1926 the company developed an even lighter and less expensive "Stable-arc" welding machine. An advertisement in the *Saturday Evening Post* touted the patented features of the "Stable-arc" welder with its continuous and uniform welding arc. It recommended it for fabrication of stronger automobile frames and seamless boilers. Through standardization Lincoln hoped to market quality products to more and more customers at lower and lower prices. Through efficient manufacturing, the company was able to reduce the cost of its welding equipment. In 1915 the 200-amp welder sold for $1,550; by 1930 the 200-amp "Stable-arc" welder sold for just $620.

MR. LINCOLN'S ADVISORY BOARD

In 1914 Lincoln organized the Advisory Board, the foundation of his evolving management philosophy. The Board convened every other Monday in Mr. Lincoln's office. Lincoln later recalled that at the end of the first meeting he told his employees matter-of-factly, "You fellows work here. I work here. There is a partnership in effort. Whatever we accomplish is going to belong to us all. Until a better man than I am shows up among you to fill my job, I'm boss. Now let's get to work and go places."[6]

The Advisory Board's purpose was to bring employees and management together for discussion "conducive to the mutual interests and welfare of the employees and management."[7] Lincoln asked the employee representatives to submit topics for discussion the Friday evening before the meeting. The board consisted of Lincoln, the factory superintendent, and elected representatives from each department or group of smaller departments, one elected foreman representative, and two elected office representatives. Each representative had one vote, and the board functioned without officers. Years later, Lincoln admitted at a meeting of managers at Ohio State University that in the beginning, he was a little "gun-shy," so he insisted on a veto, but in 30 years, he had never used it.[8] Representatives served for a year's term and were prohibited from serving more than

This 400 amp double operator "Stable-arc" welder featured a Buda six-cylinder gas engine suitable for welding in the field.

two consecutive terms. In the early years, they received $10 in compensation for each meeting. After the meeting, Lincoln personally prepared the minutes of the board. He posted them in a prominent spot near the entrance to the factory for all employees to read.

One of the elements of what historians refer to as "welfare capitalism," the idea of employee representation, gained popularity in the post-World War I era, though a number of companies adopted councils much earlier. For example, the American Rolling Mill Company (Armco), a steel supplier, set up a representative council in 1904 and may have served as a model for Lincoln Electric's Advisory Board.[9] During World War I the War Labor Board, fearing labor unrest, ordered key defense companies to adopt shop councils. After the war, many more companies established councils, including Youngstown Sheet and Tube, International Harvester, Goodyear Tire & Rubber, and Yale & Towne Manufacturing. In general, however, the welfare capitalism of the 1920s was a phenomenon limited to large companies employing over 5,000 workers. Management touted these councils as the means to promote not only fairness and cooperation between labor and management, but also greater efficiency, quality, and elimination of waste.[10]

Shop councils were the creation of management, not workers. They often dealt with minor demands, diverting attention from bread-and-butter issues, like wages and hours. Critics have argued that when the councils did achieve wage increases, they often reflected no more than management's adjustment of wages to prevailing rates. By giving workers a mechanism through which they could express their grievances and, in theory, negotiate higher wages, they made unions less attractive to employees. Indeed, during the prosperous 1920s union organizing seemed on the wane as the wages and standards of living for most workers rose. However, in the early 1930s, when the Depression forced employers to cut wages, welfare capitalism foundered and the relations between employers and their workers turned adversarial.[11] Other companies abandoned their employee representation plans in response to the labor unrest and government legislation of the 1930s, but Lincoln Electric's Advisory Board continued to flourish. It may have succeeded where others failed because it was part of a philosophy of management that transcended the paternalism of welfare capitalism. Lincoln's stress on fairness and honesty and his reward for individual performance appealed to the self-interest of his workers. He did not overestimate their devotion to the company. He insisted that his management principles should gain their respect and allegiance as a matter of "intelligent selfishness." Not only that, they made good business sense. Whatever applied to people within the company also applied in the company's dealings in the marketplace. "Fair dealing and common honesty are not only legal but are fundamentally the best policy," he wrote in *Lincoln's Incentive System*. "It may be added also that they are usually profitable."[12]

Lincoln recognized the symbolic importance of personally presiding over the Advisory Board meetings. At each meeting, he always asked each representative in turn if he or she had anything to bring up. The Advisory Board considered suggestions, criticisms, even gripes – whatever the members found of sufficient importance to bring before it either on their own initiative or at the request of one of the workers they represented. No one was ever censured or rebuffed. Lincoln's formidable presence alone served to discourage brash questions. One long-time employee recalled that Lincoln had a way of raising his voice in response to an inappropriate question that "made you pull in your ears."[13] Representatives respected him. They accepted his judgment. Clearly, though always willing to listen, Mr. Lincoln had the last word.

At a time when few companies offered workers paid vacations, the Advisory Board got Lincoln to agree to shut down the plant in August for two weeks every year so that the entire factory could take a vacation. He also responded to some unusual one-time requests. For example, he agreed to close down at noon on April 15, 1929, for opening day of the Cleveland Indians baseball season. Lincoln made concessions he thought would improve the morale or material circumstances of his workers. In other respects he had a tight-fisted attitude that gave the company a spartan atmos-

phere. Representatives objected in the late 1930s that the steam locomotive that drove into the plant created noxious fumes and cold drafts from the open doors in winter. In this instance, he refused to reroute the train, telling them that cleaner diesel locomotives about to be introduced would solve this problem. He put off having the factory windows washed with the rationale that dirt served as insulation making the plant cooler in summer, warmer in winter. To stifle complaints about how hot or cold the plant was, Lincoln appeared on the factory floor in shirtsleeves in winter, but sported a coat and vest on the hottest days of the summer. He resisted paving the muddy parking lot and refused for many years to allow the unnecessary expense of placing employees' paychecks in envelopes. He did not approve of coffee breaks and expected the company cafeteria to operate at a profit, though the operation did not have to pay overhead costs. Lincoln encouraged Advisory Board members to suggest ways to streamline operations, improve productivity, and settle complaints. Service on the Advisory Board reinforced the principles of incentive management. Lincoln always set aside time to discuss company strategy and to explain management problems and decisions. Jerry Hinkel, who came to Lincoln Electric straight out of high school and worked his way up in the company, recalled: "I heard Mr. Lincoln reiterate the basics about how to run a business over and over again. For forty-three years I'm learning by repetition. Earn as you learn. I was learning good sound business principles." Lincoln, he said, was the "master of oversimplification" and he kept his promises. The rules were clear and understood.[14]

Incentive management is the reason for the company's legendary productivity and stature in the business community.

Although the Board focused on the day-to-day problems of running the company, it also played an important role in the formulation of policy. From the exchange of ideas between the Board and Mr. Lincoln, the company's distinctive business philosophy and practice

Lincoln Advisory Board, 1943.

began to evolve: group life insurance (1915), employees association (1919), paid vacations (1923), employee stock ownership (1925), a suggestion system (1929), the bonus (1934), annuities for retired employees (1936), the merit rating (1947), and guaranteed continuous employment (1958). The practice of "promotion from within" dated from the 1920s, though it did not become a policy until 1974.

Lincoln tackled the running of his factory with the same vigor and unbounded enthusiasm that he had shown on the football field. He set out to change workers' attitudes toward their jobs. In his view, workers were not machines, but creative beings for whom self respect and recognition were as important as money. He believed that the relationship between the boss and his workers must be founded on mutual respect – that "all managers must labor and all labor must manage." That relationship need not become adversarial if each lived by the Golden Rule of treating others as he or she would like to be treated.

Each individual, he believed, had latent natural abilities that needed only the proper environment to be unleashed. He often quoted William James, one of the heroes of America's Progressive era: "The human individual lives actually far within his limits. He possesses powers of various sorts which he habitually fails to use. He energizes below his maximum and he behaves below his optimum."[15] As much as he believed that individuals had within themselves untapped wellsprings of creativity, Lincoln was no Pollyanna. He thought that Darwinian survival of the fittest applied not only to animal evolution, but also to human beings and the progressive development of their social structures. Competition weeded out lazy and incompetent workers the same way that it forced weak competitors out of business.

Lincoln encouraged communication not only through the Advisory Board, but also through a management council he instituted in 1919.

Lincoln encouraged communication not only through the Advisory Board, but also through a management council he instituted in 1919. Its purpose was to get the engineers directly involved in manufacturing. The council consisted of seven key men. It met every Saturday at noon. He stressed that it was not a "buck party," but a serious attempt to "have the technical and practical meet." Lincoln believed that factory supervisors and engineers had to work together to come up with the most efficient production methods. He made it clear that these meetings were open to anyone with suggestions, including foremen and workers. "Whole hearted cooperation on this between the men will result in tremendous savings for the company and economies for yourself," he wrote in one of his early memos.[16]

KEEPING SCORE WITH PIECEWORK

Exactly when Lincoln instituted the piecework system is unclear. Company publications from the 1940s state that J. F. Lincoln introduced piecework in 1914, though the 1920s seems more likely.[17] Lincoln thought piecework reinforced the relationship between productivity and money earned. The higher a worker's output, the more he or she earned. Lincoln considered piecework a means of keeping score in the industrial game. He disapproved of hourly wages in the factory because they provided no incentive to increase output. He thought that it was up to management to determine the most efficient way to do a particular task. The time study expert set the standard used to measure performance. The operator of a particular machine competed like an athlete to meet or beat that standard. Pay reflected ability to excel at that particular job.

In the late nineteenth century some capitalists had abused the piecework system. They had used it to exploit vulnerable immigrant laborers in sweatshops and factories. The foreman often cut the piecework price as soon as an individual worker increased output. This destroyed any incentive for the worker to strive for better performance on the job. After the turn of the century, however, piecework achieved new respectability through the advocacy of Frederick Winslow Taylor, whose ideas on scientific management began to influence management in the teens and 1920s. Part of the attraction of scientific management was the promise of replacing skilled workers, who tended to be unionized, with less costly labor, who could be trained on the job.[18]

The cornerstone of Taylor's system was what he called the "differential piece rate." Taylor recommended setting a piece rate through careful time study. A time study expert broke a specific job down into its constituent parts. He timed these parts and studied how to eliminate any unnecessary motions. Then he did the job himself in order to set a minimum time for a particular job. Taylor's incentive system rewarded individual performance. The more skilled a particular worker, the more likely he was to beat the time set by the time study man – the better the performance, the higher the paycheck. Since the piece rate had been set "scientifically" through time and motion studies, the employer had no justification to cut the piece rate unless the nature of the job radically changed.

Taylor thought that his incentive-wage system would discourage labor unions, since the more motivated workers would prefer a wage system in which their efforts were rewarded directly by higher pay. Piecework was really a customized contract between the employer and employee. It discouraged workers from thinking of themselves as a class and reinforced the idea that through performance, the worker controlled his or her destiny within the company.[19] Early company records that might have shed light on the mechanics of how Lincoln's piecework system evolved are lost, but according to oral tradition, it appears that Lincoln did not force piecework on his workers. He asked a lathe operator if he would try it out. As soon as the other workers saw that the system could dramatically increase their wages, they clamored to be part of the experiment.

Piecework left the door open for workers to use their imaginations to find better ways to do their jobs. Lincoln thought workers had a right to the increased wages earned as a result of their performance. Applying Taylor's idea of a contract between manager and worker, he emphasized that piecework could stimulate incentive only if management resisted the temptation to change the rate when the worker broke the standard set by the time study department. He wrote: "Piecework cannot and must not reduce earnings that are the result of greater skill or progress from any source developed by the man himself no matter how much he earns. Glorify and do not punish the record breaker. He is the hope of the future."[20]

Piecework left the door open for workers to use their imaginations to find better ways to do their jobs.

To introduce piecework, every job in the company had to be evaluated to determine its value relative to other jobs using criteria such as skill, responsibility, education, physical effort, and working conditions. Based on the job evaluation, the company established an hourly job base wage rate. Then, wherever practical, the job base rate was converted to a specific piecework price through a time study. The time study formally established a production standard or production rate that an average Lincoln worker could sustain on a regular basis. It was expected that experienced and expert workers would produce above the standard and that inexperienced or less capable workers would, at least at first, produce below the standard. Both the base rate and the piecework price were then fixed in company records. Once set the company could not change the piecework price just because a worker was making too much money. It was understood that the company could unilaterally change the piecework price when there was a change in method, tooling, or materials. If a worker did not agree, he or she was free to challenge the piecework price. Once a challenge had been made, the method in use was reviewed and the job retimed. If challenged a second time, the time study man had to do the job for a day and his rate became the new standard. Failure to make the standard he had previously set resulted in disgrace and immediate transfer. However, this rarely happened because Lincoln chose only the most skilled workers to staff the time study department. Company records from the time study department reveal that Lincoln personally timed two punch press jobs in the early 1930s to establish the standard.

To further motivate his workers, Lincoln offered them a choice. They could choose to reap their rewards through higher daily wages earned as a result of greater productivity, or they could suggest a new method to do their jobs. After implementation of a new method, the time study expert retimed the job and established a new piecework price. People who made suggestions that saved the company money directly through increased efficiency were entitled to receive 50 percent of the net savings for the year immediately following the adoption of the suggestion. Managers and people in time study, production control, or engineering departments could not participate. As the debates recorded in the Advisory Board minutes reveal, the suggestion system never worked perfectly. It was difficult to calculate the awards and sometimes a rejected suggestion later paid off for someone else. Nevertheless, it reflected Lincoln's desire to reward individual initiative. For example, a suggestion that the company use UPS instead of Railway Express for small shipments saved the company several thousand dollars. The worker who proposed the change received a check for $1,653 representing 50 percent of the savings to the company that year.[21]

The pace of piecework did not compromise quality under the Lincoln system, since workers were not paid for defective pieces. Workers learned to watch for less than perfect work as the product came down the line. Defects caused by others could affect their own ability to "make out," or beat the piecework rate. Though debated at various times since 1914, piecework still motivates workers as well as measures their efficiency at Lincoln Electric. Today there are over 70,000 different piecework prices in the main Cleveland factory.

THE COMING REVOLUTION

J. F. Lincoln thought his salesmen had a special mission to promote arc welding. "The sales force exists," he wrote, "because the company wants a militant driving and hard-hitting force to bring about the change from existing methods to electric arc welding practice."[22] They were the advance men in what Lincoln perceived as the coming revolution in metal fabrication techniques. The company's salesmen sold not only hardware, but also arc welding know-how. Lincoln recommended they find ways to visit their customers' factories to study their manufacturing processes. He urged his salesmen to refuse to accept the *status quo*. They should take seriously the obligation to push "civilization along a little further toward better things."[23] They must overcome the inertia and resistance of industrial designers. He told them to think about welding whenever they saw a railroad car, concrete mixer, or other riveted metal product that could be better fabricated using welding. Eventually, he predicted, designers would recognize the crudeness and inefficiency of riveting metals together. Riveting required about 40 percent more metal to compensate for the weakening of the structure caused by putting holes in it. Grey iron castings also lacked the tensile strength of welded steel. According to Lincoln, it was an economic law that as soon as a lower-cost technique for performing the same operation became available, a manufacturer that failed to adopt it would eventually go out of business.

Advertisement for a Lincoln Arc Welder, 1919.

Winning wider acceptance for arc welding was an uphill battle. In 1917 only four American companies offered arc welding machinery for sale: Wilson Welder & Metals Company, Lincoln Electric, Westinghouse, and Hobart. Lincoln often recounted how during World War I he had gone to the admiral of the Emergency Fleet Corporation with the suggestion that welding the hulls of ships could save time and money. The admiral had sneered. "Lincoln, that is all nonsense. You can't weld ships. I would undertake to kick off with my foot any welding you could do."[24] This perception began to change after welding equipment companies demonstrated to the Navy that welding could drastically reduce the time required for complicated repairs. German crews had sabotaged fifteen ships stranded in New York harbor after the declaration of war. These ships were returned to service within months as Allied troop transports, their broken drive shafts and other essential metal parts welded back together.[25]

Though perceived merely as a repair process at that time, the need for building transport ships in a hurry prompted the Navy to investigate welding as an alternative to the prevailing method of riveting in ship assembly. A special committee set up by the Emergency Fleet Corporation and headed by Comfort Adams of Harvard University, went to England to investigate British methods. They discovered that the British were using welding in a variety of manufacturing processes, including the construction of a ship with an all-welded hull. The ship was launched in 1920.

To assist in coping with the shortage of trained arc welders during the war, the Electric Welding Branch of the Education and Training Section of the Emergency Fleet Corporation supported the creation of welding schools in Cleveland, Schenectady, Brooklyn, and Philadelphia. The school in Cleveland, run by The Lincoln Electric Company, operated day and night throughout the war to transform American enlisted men into skilled welders. At the end of the war about twenty members of the Wartime Welding Committee, along with Lincoln, H. M. Hobart, James Burke, D. H. Wilson, and Herman Lemp, organized the American Welding Society. Comfort Adams served as the society's first president with J. M. Morehead, prominent in the oxyacetylene industry, as vice president. The Society functioned as a technical society, not a trade association. It worked to establish welding standards and specifications for the industry.[26]

Though they attempted to work together in the Welding Society, manufacturers of arc welding equipment and the competing oxyacetylene process were fierce rivals at this time. Commercial applications for oxyacetylene gas were developed shortly after the turn of the century. Carl Linde, a professor of mechanics at the Technical Institute in Munich, Germany, and Georges Claude, an electrical engineer who founded Compagnie Française de l'Acétylène Dissous (progenitor of Air Liquide), both invented different methods of generating and storing oxyacetylene gas in metal cylinders. This gas, a combination of oxygen and acetylene, did not become successful commercially until processes for large-scale production were developed. In 1906 Myron T. Herrick, president of Cleveland's Society for Savings, and several wealthy friends bought the American rights to Linde's process. In 1917 Linde Air Products combined with four other American oxyacetylene companies to form the Union Carbide and Carbon Company. Linde's competitor, the Air Reduction Company, Inc. was organized by Percy A. Rockefeller and Robert C. Pruyn in 1915 through a licensing agreement with Air Liquide.[27] The oxyacetylene process, first used on a large scale for welding and flame cutting during World War I, dominated the welding market through the 1920s. It was used for a variety of applications in the rail, automotive, and steel industries.

During World War I arc welding was limited to welding steel plate. Oxyacetylene continued to be a superior process for welding brass, aluminum, and cast iron. High on J. F. Lincoln's agenda was the development of arc welding to the point where it could compete with oxyacetylene. In 1919 he issued a series of confidential communications on sales strategy to Lincoln salesmen. One memo, consisting of an article by R. E. Kinkead, reprinted from the October 1919 *Welding Engineer,* discussed how to sell arc welding equipment to commercial weldors, known as "job shop men."

Commercial weldors repaired factory equipment, farm machinery, stoves, and other appliances. They also subcontracted with manufacturers to do special welding jobs. Kinkead warned that the arc welding salesman should not assume that just because his prospect is dressed in dirty overalls he "is an ignoramus and is a 'dead one' from the shoulders up."[28] The job shop weldor certainly knew that oxyacetylene produced stronger welds. The real advantage of arc welding, according to the Kinkead article, was its lower cost.

THE ARC WELDING GOSPEL

James F. Lincoln set out to change the perception of arc welding. Beyond its use in repair, he wanted arc welding to become a production process, essential to all types of metal fabrication. At first, he recalled, "there was hardly enough business to stuff a gnat's eye." Looking back on the growth of the industry from the vantage of World War II, he said: "It was spun from the base spool of giving more value for less money, and the result is an industry that makes jobs for thousands."[29] Lincoln's closest associate in the company was probably Alton Frank (Charlie) Davis. Davis played a key role in the effort to spread the gospel of arc welding. Born in 1889 in Diamond, Ohio, Davis was the son of a postmaster, keeper of a country store and livery stable, and Portage County's best known auctioneer. After two years at Mount Union College and two years in the engineering department of the city of Alliance, he entered Ohio State University. He graduated with a degree in electrical engineering in 1914. During a visit to Ohio State, Lincoln hired him. After giving Davis a 20-minute tour of the Cleveland plant, Lincoln sent him to Chicago to sell Lincoln equipment. After several years as the sales manager for the Chicago office, he returned to Cleveland to take charge of the Cleveland

In the 1920s, J.F. Lincoln envisioned arc welding as a revolutionary process to make bonding any kind of metal cheaper, faster, and stronger.

Trade show, 1927. This display featured a Lincoln motor submerged in a tank, run continuously since 1909.

sales office and handle public relations. He became vice president in charge of educational and promotional activities in 1925. When he contracted tuberculosis, usually a fatal disease before antibiotics, Lincoln told him to go and get well, and he continued to pay his salary. He returned to the company after a year and a half with the same enthusiasm for his educational mission.

In the company's first book on arc welding, *Arc Welding: the New Age in Iron and Steel,* Charlie Davis reached out to designers in industry with the simple message that arc welding offered a superior method to join metals at a lower cost. His text appeared in 1926, the same year Linde Air Products Company came out with a book promoting sheet metal welding by the competing oxyacetylene process. Davis recommended the replacement of cast iron with arc welded steel. Cast iron, he pointed out, was difficult to weld because its high carbon content made it brittle. Steel had important advantages. It cost one-third as much per pound as cast iron. It was a more uniform product, six times stronger in tension and two and a half times stiffer than cast iron. In the past designers had preferred cast iron because it could be made into any shape. Davis pointed out that welded steel offered far greater design flexibility at a fraction of the cost. It required no casting pattern, lower material inventory, fewer obsolete parts, little or no machining, and less building space. He claimed it was only tradition that kept designers from seizing upon the potential of arc welded steel for hundreds of applications. The advantages of arc welding were simple and compelling: "The shop superintendent or designer who does not know arc welding is probably losing money for his firm. He is authorizing drilling, punching, reaming, bolting and riveting where arc welding will do the work better and cheaper. He is using iron castings where arc-welded steel would be cheaper and stronger."[30]

By the mid-1920s the welding revolution had not yet occurred. Yet Davis believed that the day was coming when noisy riveting would be obsolete. Welding could make bridges, skyscrapers, and ships safer and stronger. "Instead of being constructed of many separate plates and shapes pegged together with rivets, the frame work of each will be one solid piece of steel welded into a homogeneous whole by the magic of the electric arc."[31] In 1926 Davis could point to only a few pioneering examples of the use of arc welding in construction. In 1919 The Lincoln Electric Company had

The Upper Carnegie Medical Building, built in 1928, was the first welded multi-story commercial building in the United States.

added a steel structure to reinforce the crumbling walls and sagging floors of the factory on Kelley Avenue. In 1923 in Toronto, Canada, a designer had boldly demonstrated that a bridge of welded steel and concrete could carry heavy traffic across three spans measuring 672 feet overall. In 1927 the architect Albert Kahn had designed a twelve-story addition to the Peoples Outfitting Company in Detroit, supported by 103 arc welded girders, and in Canton, Ohio, the Peerless Auto Sales Company had built a welded two-story structure.

In 1928 Lincoln Electric joined forces with the Austin Company in Cleveland to use arc welding in the steel framework of the Upper Carnegie Building in downtown Cleveland. The Austin Company built the four-story structure at its own expense as an experiment to see whether it could be fabricated entirely without bolts or rivets.[32] All the welding was supervised and carried out by Lincoln employees using Lincoln's Stable-arc electrodes. The elimination of rivets reduced the steel requirements by 15 percent and allowed designers to pioneer the use of continuous beams the entire length of the building. Welded lattice joists allowed them to conceal pipes between floors. However, the experiment was not entirely successful because the building required a great deal of shoring to hold the steel girders in place. As the first welded multi-story commercial building in the United States, the Upper Carnegie Building helped to promote welding as the new "silent" process to replace the obnoxious noise of riveted construction. The Austin Company, like J. F. Lincoln, believed in the future of arc welding. In the 1930s it launched an advertising campaign that touted Austin's arc-welded factory structures as "the beginning of a new era in the building art."[33]

As the first welded multi-story commercial building in the United States, the Upper Carnegie Building helped to promote welding as the new "silent" process to replace the obnoxious noise of riveted construction.

Another marketing effort focused on promoting arc welding widely among industry's decision makers. The Lincoln Electric Company joined with other welding companies in 1929 to run a series of advertisements in popular magazines like *Time, Business Week*, and *Nation's Business* on the theory that after a day's work and a good dinner the boss would sit down with his cigar and be ready for arc welding's message. The advertisements featured a monumental welding operator clenching an electrode holder in one hand and a fistful of electrodes in the other, with the

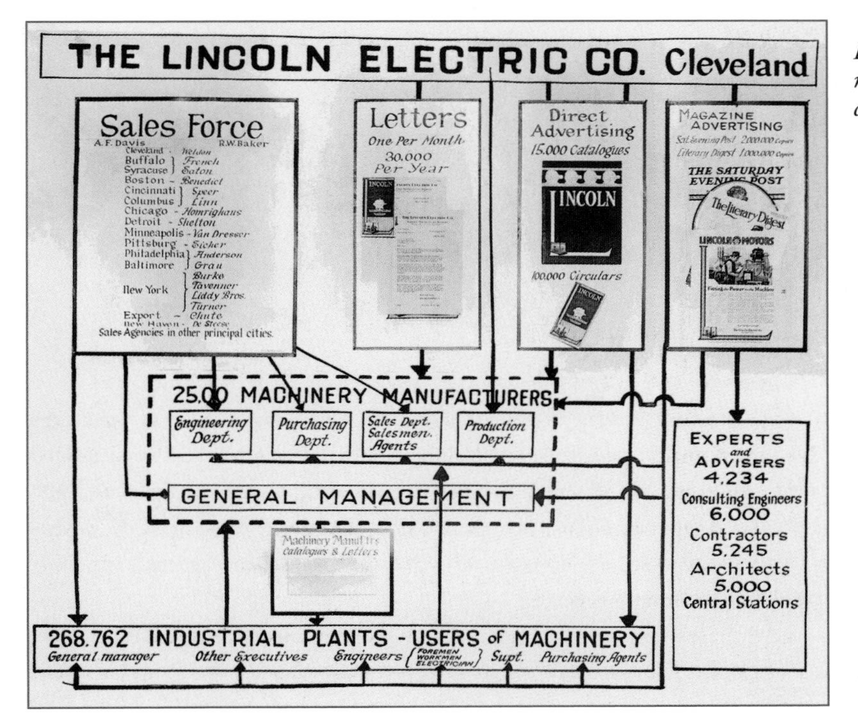

Lincoln Electric's marketing plan, circa 1920s.

caption, "I am Arc Welding. My Platform is Steel. My Creed is Progress." A steel mill, the backbone of America's industrialization, filled the background.

Despite these efforts to promote arc welding, the field grew slowly. Although mainly a repair technique, the process began to be used to build pressure vessels and storage tanks for fuel oil, gasoline, and petroleum distillates, and in the fabrication of blowers, fans, air conduits, and bases for machine tools. When the first welded pipeline was constructed by the Philadelphia & Suburban Gas Company in 1911, oxyacetylene was used, but by the 1920s some steam and water pipelines were being arc welded.[34] However, the process was not entirely satisfactory because oxidation of the bare welding rod made the welds brittle. Though generally preferred for work outdoors because it did not require the transport of heavy gas cylinders, arc welding on a large scale, particularly for natural gas and oil pipelines, did not become widespread until the development of the coated electrode in the 1930s.

THE MAN BEHIND THE MASK

Charlie Davis believed the future of welding lay in the operator's hand. Manual welding requires a high degree of hand-eye coordination complicated by the need to wear a mask to protect the eyes from the arc's blinding light. Welding for the first time is an act of blind faith. Because of the darkened glass of the mask, there is no way to see the hand before contact of the electric arc with a metal plate is made. This is called "striking the arc." In the early days of arc welding it took considerable skill to "hold the arc," keeping it as short as possible without actually touching the metal plate. Experienced operators guarded the tricks of their trade. Their "beads" – the metal deposited during the welding process – were their signatures, each a distinctive reflection of their mastery of the art.

Davis realized that it was important not only to promote arc welding in metal design and construction, but also to raise technical standards. Without the formal organization of weldors on a craft basis, it was difficult to enforce qualifications.[35] Publicity often drew attention to failures resulting from incompetent arc welding technique. These failures made it more difficult to win wider acceptance for the process. To expand welding knowledge and break down the guild-like secrecy practiced by weldors, in 1926 Charlie Davis began to write and edit a special magazine "published for those who take pride in their jobs." The *Stabilizer®* was an immediate success. Davis encouraged readers to share problems, techniques, and tips with their fellow operators. Popular columns like "How can I do it?" and "How I did it!" from the "boys in the field" spread welding knowledge. Davis asked each operator to "unload his mind." In the first issue, he wrote: "If you have a question in your think tank that you want cleared up – we'll print it in here and let the other fellows who have similar problems answer it for you."[36] Each issue contained the "Lincoln Pledge." The pledge consisted of six precepts intended to promote the highest welding standards. Operators promised to:

Welding fabrication technique, about 1920.

First. To do all in my power to advance the cause of arc welding.

Second. Never to be guilty of knowingly making a poor weld.

Third. To report to my superior immediately any weld which I believe is not thoroughly dependable for the service for which it is intended.

Fourth. To give to my employer, at all times, all my best efforts, loyal service, and honest workmanship.

Fifth. To extend all possible assistance to welders less proficient than myself.

Sixth. To strive each day to increase my knowledge and skill in the art of arc welding.

Volume 1
Number 1

August, 1926

The Operator's

STABILIZER

Published for operators who take pride in their jobs

I THINK that although the word "I" is the smallest word in the English language, it is also our biggest word. The whole advancement of industry is based on "I."

For if I don't do my job well and if you (you're an I) don't do your job well, and if all the other I's don't do their jobs well—what a setback this old world would take.

That's why I've put a big I in the name of this little helper—for its purpose is to give each "I" in the welding game the benefit of the other I's experience.

Then each of us will do a better job—and welding will become a still more important factor in manufacturing.

What we want to accomplish is a mutual admiration society so that we'll all get a kick out of it. Well, it's up to you fellows—you charter members of the I Society.

It's Up to You

IF THIS little publication is going to be worth a tinker's dam—it's all up to you.

Each one of you operators has behind his shield the very stuff that will make these pages SING.

We don't want the STABILIZER to *preach*—we want it to *teach*.

So unload your mind.

If you have a question in your think tank that you want cleared up—we'll print it in here and let the other fellows who have had similar problems answer it for you.

If you've done some unusual stunts with your welder, don't let the fact die—send it in with the roughest kind of a sketch and we'll doctor up your art and print it in the "How-I-Did-It" page—you ought to get credit for it—and you *will* here.

The front office fellows have their conventions where they interchange ideas on the conduct of business.

Let's make the STABILIZER a regular and frequent convention of the boys doing the real work in welding.

A. F. DAVIS,
EDITOR.

DOWN IN THIS CORNER *each issue I want to publish the picture of some operator who has done, or is doing, a real worth-while job.*

Mr. S. P. Rodoany (whose picture appears this time), is the man who did the field welding on the First Commercial All-Welded Steel Building at Canton, Ohio, which was erected by The Morgan Engineering Company of Alliance, Ohio.

If anyone knows of an operator whose work entitles him to his picture here, send me his name and address.

First page of the first Stabilizer.

Within a year of the magazine's founding over 1,000 weldors had signed the Lincoln Pledge. The company returned to each operator an engraved certificate, suitable for framing. They could also buy a special tie pin or watch fob with the "Stable-arc" insignia. From a readership of 200 in 1926, circulation of the *Stabilizer* climbed to 75,000 in 1930. The company considered the *Stabilizer* not only a vehicle for building solidarity among weldors and promoting better welding technique, but also a key marketing tool. The minutes of the Junior Board for 1944 state: "The *Stabilizer* is considered by the Board and by all those with whom we have been in contact as one of the fundamental reasons behind the general operator's preference for our products."[37] By 1948 the magazine had over 100,000 subscribers. Today its readers number about 130,000.

BUILDING A MANAGEMENT TEAM

With faith in his employees' natural desire for self-improvement, Lincoln encouraged competition, or what he called "game spirit" in the factory. His incentive system rewarded merit and weeded out incompetent or lazy employees who did not make the team. Lincoln promoted from within. He had the available positions posted on the bulletin board at the factory entrance and anyone could try out for any position. Workers who moved into management had "won their places as managers in open competition."[38] Lincoln believed that to develop good managers, it was necessary to give them jobs that were over their heads and then to keep the pressure on. "This is not slave driving," he wrote. "It gives instead a feeling of accomplishment, which is our greatest satisfaction."[39] He called upon Charlie Davis, Clarence Taylor, and George Landis to give extraordinary service to the company. Through their efforts the company took shape.

Clarence Taylor played a significant role as vice president in charge of sales. Lincoln hired him in 1916 on the conviction that the competition relished by athletes on the playing field served them well in business. A former captain of the Western Reserve University football team, Taylor started as a $60-a-month factory clerk. He served in the Army Air Corps during World War I, then returned to Lincoln Electric where he took the position of assembly and test foreman. Lincoln promoted him to the time study department, then factory superintendent, where he experimented with various cost-cutting methods on the assembly line. In 1928, while he was on the roof of the factory talking to a roofing contractor, Lincoln bounded up the ladder to tell him he was to take over as vice president of sales for the company. Though Taylor objected that he was a "fact man who didn't know a talking point from fish bait," he organized the sales force that by 1942 had grown to 90 salesmen, most of whom were college graduates with engineering degrees.[40] Roland Sharer, who pulled in a contract for equipment to weld Sherman Tanks at Wright Field in 1937 and later headed the Columbus sales office, recalled that Taylor inspired the sales division with the principles of incentive management. "He gave people a lot of latitude and encouraged them to come up with new ideas."[41] Following World War II, after a clash with J. F. Lincoln, Taylor resigned. He launched a second career as executive director of the Cleveland Clinic, Inc.

Engineer George Landis also left his mark on the company. Between 1916 and 1918 he had studied at Dickinson College in Carlisle, Pennsylvania, to prepare for a career as a Methodist minister. His life soon took a different turn. World War I found him in the Navy working as a radio operator. Upon discharge he took a degree in electrical engineering at Ohio State University and headed for General Electric, then moved on to Westinghouse, selling farm lighting plants and later central station equipment in the district office in Cleveland. Attracted by Lincoln's charisma, he accepted a position at Lincoln Electric in the experimental department in 1923. At that time he was one of two engineers in the company. In 1930 Lincoln named him chief engineer. During the next ten years, he obtained fifty-one patents related to welding machinery. He worked on a high-frequency alternating current motor-generator welder with improved welding characteristics. He also developed a 60-cycle transformer for small welders that made it possible to use lower open circuit voltage. His effort to develop low-cost motor-generator sets gave the company a product with mass-market appeal. The fluid insulation he perfected for stationary transformers, introduced during winding by a dipping process, made higher operating temperatures possible. Another member of the early management team, J. W. Meriam, left a secure banking job in 1914. He helped Lincoln put the company on a firm financial footing and served as corporate secretary of the company until his retirement in 1934 when Charlie Davis took over his job.

During the years that Lincoln's ideas on incentive management began to take shape, he had only two interests outside the company – the Presbyterian Church and Ohio State University. Both gave him important opportunities to develop leadership qualities. In 1920 Lincoln chaired the pulpit committee of the Old First Presbyterian Church of East Cleveland. His charge was to find a new minister for the church. Lincoln drove up to a small church in upstate New York. Unannounced, he heard Frank Halliday Ferris deliver a stirring sermon. Afterwards, Lincoln stopped at the local tavern where he asked the proprietor's opinion of Ferris's character. Not a church-goer himself, he

> During the years that Lincoln's ideas on incentive management began to take shape, he had only two interests outside the company – the Presbyterian Church and Ohio State University.

admitted, he nevertheless contributed $25 a year to Ferris's church. This assured Lincoln that he had found his man. He immediately offered Ferris the job, typically confident that the board of elders would fall in behind his decision.[42] Ferris and Lincoln developed a close personal friendship, meeting each week over Sunday night supper to discuss the respective institutions they served and to hammer out their ideas in each others' company. Ferris described Lincoln as a man for whom "the heart of Christianity was the Sermon on the Mount and especially the Golden Rule which he said was just enlightened selfishness."[43]

Lincoln often acknowledged Ferris's influence on the development of his ideas on incentive management. For example, in a letter to Lincoln, Ferris offered a quotation from William James as a text for one of Lincoln's business "sermons": "The real wealth of a nation is the number of superior men it contains. No price is too high to pay for a great statesman or captain of industry. Geniuses are ferments... when they come together, the whole population seems to share in the higher energy which they awaken... The effects are pervasive and momentous."[44] Ferris, like Lincoln, wrote prolifically. He published articles in the *Atlantic Monthly* and *Harpers* and produced a book, *Standing Up to Life*, in 1953. After serving a congregation in Newark, New Jersey, for several years in the late 1920s, Ferris returned to take the post of pastor of the Fairmount Presbyterian Church in Cleveland Heights from 1931 to 1950. Lincoln walked down Fairmount Boulevard every Sunday morning from his home in Shaker Heights, rain or shine, to listen to, and no doubt critique, Ferris's weekly sermon. He also generously supported Fairmount Church, at that time attended by many of Cleveland's prominent business leaders. At the completion of a new sanctuary, Lincoln donated an organ in memory of his mother, Frances Louisa Marshall Lincoln, remembered perhaps for her sacrifices as the wife of the maverick William Elleby Lincoln. When Fairmount Church added a new wing, Lincoln made sure it had arc-welded beams.

In 1927 the alumni of Ohio State University elected the former football star (who had never graduated) president of the Alumni Association. Lincoln relished this job, and rarely failed to return to his alma mater for football games in the fall. Certainly, the games brought back glorious memories of OSU's "flying wedge. "I never smell the odor of burning leaves, or of stale sweat," he wrote in the alumni magazine, "without its bringing vividly to mind memories of the Armory, the old concrete swimming tank, and old Ohio field and the athletic struggles there."[45]

Lincoln believed the function of the OSU Alumni Advisory Board was to give constructive criticism to the university, and he used the president's column in the alumni magazine to hone his writing skills and to play the role of devil's advocate. With the secretary of the association, J. L. Morrill (later president of the University of Minnesota), he organized the Ohio State University Research Foundation, Inc. and financed the first two years of its pilot operation. In 1939 he served as a member of the organizing committee for the Ohio State University Development Fund and helped to raise funds for university housing and a Student Loan Foundation. He also contributed money for the creation of the department of welding engineering at Ohio State University, making it one of the few universities in the country to offer a degree in welding engineering. He gave generously to the department of electrical engineering, chaired by Erwin E. Dreese, who later headed the James F. Lincoln Arc Welding Foundation. He encouraged Ohio State graduates, particularly athletes, to apply for jobs at Lincoln Electric. In addition to Lincoln's right-hand men, George Landis and Charlie Davis, they included Michael N. Vuchnich, Jack Roscoe, Frank Boucher, and Al Patnik, all of whom started as Lincoln salesmen and later became executives of the company.

Welding a ball and spigot joint with Stable Arc welding rods, circa 1920s.

In 1927, with the company on a solid financial basis, the board of directors voted to reduce the price of motors and welders.[46] The following year, John Lincoln named J. F. Lincoln president of the company, while he continued as chairman of the board. As the new president, James F. Lincoln could look back with satisfaction on the management system he had set in place. He had created a work environment that workers accepted as fair and reasonable. Piecework encouraged efficiency and rewarded performance. Through the Advisory Board he could communicate effectively with his workers and they had the opportunity to voice their criticisms and contribute their ideas for better management. In contrast to the conspicuous consumption and more visible philanthropy of prominent Clevelanders in the 1920s, J. F. Lincoln remained a man of simple tastes with an intense loyalty to employees, his church, and his alma mater. The Depression years would enlarge the focus of his activities. He would become an outspoken adversary of the New Deal, a zealous Republican, and a prominent spokesman for the arc welding industry.

[1] Quoted by Charles Herbruck in the introduction to James F. Lincoln, *A New Approach to Industrial Economics* (New York: Devin-Adair, 1961), 8. See also Eugene Gay-Tifft, "The Career of James Finney Lincoln," *Railroad Workers Journal*, January-February 1946, 3-12.

[2] Loose leaf notebook, Nov. 11, 1918, LEC archives.

[3] James F. Lincoln, *Selling Helps for Lincoln Salesmen* (Cleveland: The Lincoln Electric Company, c. 1924), 44.

[4] *Saturday Evening Post*, March 7, 1925.

[5] The new machine had the protection of the so-called Homrighaus patents, filed February 26, 1915, and granted August 28, 1917.

[6] Eugene Gay-Tifft, 8.

[7] *Constitution and By-Laws of the Advisory Board of The Lincoln Electric Co.*, reprint of January, 1941. LEC archives. It appears that J. F. Lincoln met informally with workers beginning in 1914, but the Advisory Board was not formally established until 1916.

[8] James F. Lincoln, "Labor Efficiency as Viewed by Top Management,"*Proceedings of the Fifth Personnel Institute*, Ohio State University, May 12, 1943.

[9] A former executive of the company has suggested that Lincoln used the American Rolling Mill Company (Armco) as a model. A brochure, "Armco Personal Relations,"by Hugh W. Wright, reprinted from *Factory Management and Maintenance*, May 1937, can be found in the LEC archives.

[10] Stuart D. Brandes, *American Welfare Capitalism*, 1880-1940 (Chicago: University of Chicago Press, 1976), 119-134. David Brody, "The Rise and Decline of Welfare Capitalism," *Workers in Industrial America: Essays in the Twentieth Century Struggle* (New York: Oxford University Press, 1980), 48-81.

[11] Brandes and Brody, above.

[12] *Lincoln's Incentive System*, 46.

[13] Interview with Joe Vinceller, April 17, 1992.

[14] Interview with Jerry Hinkel, Feb. 10, 1993.

[15] *Lincoln's Incentive System*, 44.

[16] Feb. 1919, Loose leaf notebook, LEC archives.

[17] See William Miskoe, "Lincoln Incentive Plan, *Rydge's*, March 1, 1946.

[18] Very little historical work has been done on the introduction of Taylorism in Cleveland. The best work on this subject is: David J. Goldberg, "Richard A. Feiss, Mary Barnett Gilson, and Scientific Management at Joseph & Feiss, 1909-1925," in *A Mental Revolution: Scientific Management since Taylor*, Daniel Nelson, ed. (Columbus: Ohio State University Press, 1992), 40-57.

[19] Sanford M. Jacoby, *Employing Bureaucracy: Managers, Unions, and the Transformation of Work in American Industry, 1900-1945* (New York: Columbia University Press, 1985), 44-46. Taylor's famous essay on piecework is "A Piece Rate System: A Step Toward Partial Solution of the Labor Problem,"*ASME Transactions* 16 (1895).

[20] *James F. Lincoln, Incentive Management: A New Approach to Human Relationships in Industry and Business* (Cleveland: The Lincoln Electric Company, 1951), 138.

[21] Arthur Todd, "Just and Unjust Rewards,"personal communication to the author, about October 1992.

[22] *Selling Helps*, 12.

[23] *Selling Helps*, 44.

[24] Naval Affairs investigating committee, May 27, 1942. Quoted in Fred. B. Barton, "They Thanked Him for Coming, " *Nation's Business*, August 1942.

[25] See *Repair of the German Ships: The Biggest Welding Repair Job in the History of the World* (New York: Wilson Welder and Metals Company, Inc.) [no date].

[26] R. D. Simonson, 104.

[27] On the oxyacetylene process see Andrew J. Butrica, *Out of Thin Air: A History of Air Products and Chemicals, Inc.*, 1940-1990 (New York: Praeger, 1990), 6-9. Also, R. D. Simonson, 51-78.

[28] "Special Welder Letter,"#24, LEC archives.

[29] Neil M. Clark, "How Much are Workers Worth?" *Saturday Evening Post*, July 24, 1943, 51.

[30] *Arc Welding: The New Age in Iron and Steel* (Cleveland: The Lincoln Electric Company, 1926) 57.

[31] *Arc Welding*, 31.

[32] Martin Greif, *The New Industrial Landscape, The Story of the Austin Company* (Clinton, NJ: The Mainstreet Press, 1978), 91.

[33] Martin Greif, 95-96.

[34] Walter Klie, "Lincoln's Genius Scores Triumph of Engineering,"*The Ohio State Monthly*, April 1926, 299-301.

[35] According to R. D. Simonson, page 102, a ruling in a 1917 rail strike that welding was a "tool rather than a trade"proved a setback for welding because it prevented organization of weldors on a craft basis, thus precluding the enforcement of standards.

[36] *Stabilizer*, August 1926.

[37] Minutes of the Junior Board of Directors, Feb. 2, 1944.

[38] James F. Lincoln, Incentive Management (Cleveland: The Lincoln Electric Company, 1951), 139.

[39] *Incentive Management*, 59.

[40] Neil M. Clark, "How Much Are Workers Worth?," *Saturday Evening Post*, July 24, 1943, 16-17, 51-52.

[41] Interview with Roland Sharer, August 4, 1993.

[42] Anecdote as related to the author by Charles Herbruck.

[43] Frank Halliday Ferris, "James F. Lincoln, 1883-1965,"Memorial Service in Fairmount Church, June 26, 1965.

[44] Frank Ferris to James F. Lincoln, March 15, 1993. Papers of Harry Carlson.

[45] J. F. Lincoln, "How Fares Now the Race?"reprinted in *The Ohio State University Monthly*, Oct. 1948, 34.

[46] Annual Meeting, March 15, 1927. LEC archives.

Chapter 3

Resilience and Expansion, 1929-1941

In October 1929 the stock market crashed, banks failed, and companies large and small foundered. The Depression threw thousands of Clevelanders out of work. People stood in bread lines, ate at soup kitchens, and went on public relief. A city with a population of 900,429 in 1930, within a year the rolls of Cleveland's jobless had swelled from 41,000 to 100,000.[1] Widespread unemployment gave new life to the labor movement, quiescent during the previous decade. Workers organized and labor relations turned surly and often violent.

In contrast to the general economic distress created by the Depression, 1929 proved a banner year for The Lincoln Electric Company, prompting a 10-for-1 split of the stock. That year a new

J.F. Lincoln in Melbourne, Australia, 1938.

coated electrode started the company's climb to dominance of the American welding industry. It combined tensile strength, high ductility, and low cost to make it greatly superior to bare wire electrodes then in general use. Named "Fleetweld 5" by Charlie Davis because the coating contained five different chemicals, the new electrode dramatically increased the speed of welding. It could be used in all positions: flat, vertical, and overhead. Fleetweld produced stronger welds because its coating, consisting principally of alpha cellulose, shielded the arc from oxygen and nitrogen of the air during the welding process. Fleetweld became the company's most successful product, a "consumable" like razor blades that found a market even during the Depression. Somewhat modified in the 1960s and now called Fleetweld 5-P, it is still on the market after almost seventy years. Though it was difficult in the 1930s to sell Lincoln welding equipment because most companies had little cash for capital improvements, the strong loyalty of weldors to Fleetweld, the electrode marked with three green dots, drove sales long after competitors had begun to manufacture comparable coated electrodes. In 1935 when the company offered dual control on its motor-generator sets to allow the operator to fine tune the arc for various applications, orders for welding machinery picked up as well. As a result of continued strong sales, in 1937 the company invested $700,000 to expand the Coit Road plant, the third addition since 1929.

Fleetweld became the company's most successful product, a "consumable" like razor blades that found a market even during the Depression.

As the company stepped up production between 1933 and 1941, the number of Lincoln Electric employees increased from 404 to 979. In the early 1930s, with so many unemployed people competing for the few available jobs, the company had the luxury of selecting only the most promising production workers from among Cleveland's large ethnic population. J. F. Lincoln insisted that everyone – even college graduates – start on the factory floor. They would be promoted only after they proved themselves. Lincoln often employed members of the same family with the rationale that they knew and would support incentive management with greater loyalty than any outsider. This policy included his own family. Lincoln's son, Jimmy Lincoln, Jr., and his sons-in-law, Kenneth Steingass, Howard Morris and Robert Wilson, would all work at various times for Lincoln Electric.[2]

J. F. Lincoln's ideas on how to solve the country's economic problems differed radically from those of Franklin D. Roosevelt. When the company showed a strong profit in 1934, J. F. Lincoln offered his own "new deal" to workers – a generous bonus that became legendary. At the same time, he and the ebullient Charlie Davis stepped up their efforts to promote the field of arc welding. By World War II, the company had become one of the country's major manufacturers of welding supplies and equipment and was ready to contribute welding know-how to the war effort.

FLEETWELD

Europeans were the first to make progress in the development of coated electrodes. It was well known that oxygen and nitrogen in the air compromised the quality of welds by making them brittle. Various mineral and organic coatings were tried to produce a protective atmosphere around the arc during the welding process. In addition to the greater ease and speed of welding, coated electrodes produced welds that were more ductile and could withstand impacts better than welds made with bare electrodes. The welds of coated electrodes were, in fact, stronger than the steel they joined. It was soon discovered that by varying the chemical composition of the coating, electrodes could be adapted for welding different metal types. Chief among the new applications for arc welding were tanks for oil, natural gas and water, and pipelines capable of withstanding the high pressures and temperatures required by oil refining.

The history of the coated electrode begins with the founding in Sweden of ESAB (Elektriska Svetsnings-Aktiebolaget) in 1904 by Oscar Kjellberg. Kjellberg developed a mineral-coated, or rutile electrode. The coating consisted of limestone, potassium carbonate, silicates, and magnesium and zirconium oxides, plus carbon. During the welding process the coating vaporized and formed a gas that kept the molten metal from coming into contact with the air as it cooled. Because the protective gas prevented harmful embrittling reactions from taking place, Kjellberg's coated electrode significantly improved the quality of the weld metal. Kjellberg applied for the patent to this invention in 1907 and received it in 1914.[3]

In 1912 Arthur Percy Strohmenger of the British Quasi-Arc Company introduced electrodes covered with an organic material – actually asbestos-impregnated string. The coating melted and fused with the molten metal to form a protective slag that shielded the weld from the damaging effects of the atmosphere. Because Quasi-Arc electrodes were wrapped with string by hand, they were expensive to manufacture. They were also difficult to use because molten sparks, called "spatter," flew off during the welding process.[4]

When World War I cut off import of European coated electrodes, the A. O. Smith Company of Milwaukee, a pressure vessel manufacturer, pursued the development of the organic-type coated electrode. A. O. Smith claimed to have developed the first electrode to "produce weld metal

In addition to the greater ease and speed of welding, coated electrodes produced welds that were more ductile and could withstand impacts better than welds made with bare electrodes.

A fistful of Fleetweld 5 electrodes, the coated electrode that carried Lincoln Electric through the Depression.

unimpaired in quality by the deleterious effects of oxygen and nitrogen" – a weld claimed to be as strong as steel parts joined by the weld.[5] Essentially paper-wrapped wire crimped at each end, these covered electrodes were produced by hand until a young chemist at A. O. Smith, John J. Chyle, discovered a process to extrude a paste-like cellulose mix onto the wire in 1926.[6] Although patented, A. O. Smith failed to seize upon the commercial implications of the new development. It was left to Lincoln Electric to reap the rewards of A. O. Smith's pioneering work.

Before the introduction of coated electrodes, The Lincoln Electric Company offered only two electrodes for sale: Kathode (later renamed Stable-arc®) and Anode. Kathode was a mild steel wire, cut to size and lightly covered with lime to stabilize the arc. It was used for welding steel plate. Anode, a bare nickel wire, had more specialized uses, such as welding cast iron. Because it was important to control the quality of the steel wire, The American Steel & Wire Company manufactured wire to Lincoln Electric's specifications. Kathode was a money-maker in the 1920s. Lincoln described how he expected demand for this electrode to grow in his "Special Welder Letter": "It is estimated that about 4,000 operators are working every day in this country with the metal electrode process. This means that 60,000 pounds of welding wire are consumed every day, or about 18,000,000 pounds per year which represents at 8 cents per pound, something over a million dollars worth of wire which is being used every year on the electric welding process in this country."[7]

About 1928, sensing the revolutionary implications of A. O. Smith's development of the coated electrode – especially if it could be mass produced – J. F. Lincoln gave Theophil Edward Jerabek, a newly hired engineer, the job of figuring out how to manufacture Lincoln Electric's first coated electrode. Jerabek had grown up one of ten children in Silver Lake, a small Minnesota town, and graduated in 1927 from the University of Minnesota with a degree in metallurgical engineering. A brilliant student who also played in the university marching band, he received the Sigma Xi prize for his thesis, "Abnormality in Steels." Jerabek set up a laboratory in the experimental department at Lincoln Electric where he built much of his equipment himself. Louis Prebevsek, a Lincoln production worker, remembered making Fleetweld 5 in about 1928 by wrapping the wire with paper by hand, rolling it in a silicate, and then drying it.[8] To figure out how to extrude a cellulose coating onto the bare wire, J. F. Lincoln took his young protégé to visit a spaghetti factory. Trial and error and T. E. Jerabek's dogged determination proved sufficient to lay the foundation for Lincoln's proprietary extrusion process. Mass production of coated electrodes would prove a key to the company's profitability through the Great Depression and World War II.

In 1929, when Lincoln Electric introduced Fleetweld 5, the welding industry had become extremely competitive.

In 1929, when Lincoln Electric introduced Fleetweld 5, the welding industry had become extremely competitive. Companies like General Electric, Westinghouse, Roebling, Una Welding, Hobart Brothers, and Murex all produced electrodes, but the superior quality and lower cost of Fleetweld 5 gave Lincoln a competitive edge. In 1930 when the A. O. Smith Company brought a $7 million suit against Lincoln Electric for infringement of its coated electrode patent, J. F. Lincoln put up a spirited fight. The suit focused particularly on Lincoln's use of alpha cellulose, the main ingredient in Fleetweld 5. For protection, several months before A. O. Smith filed its suit, Lincoln Electric purchased the rights to the patents of an obscure inventor, George W. Cravens. Cravens

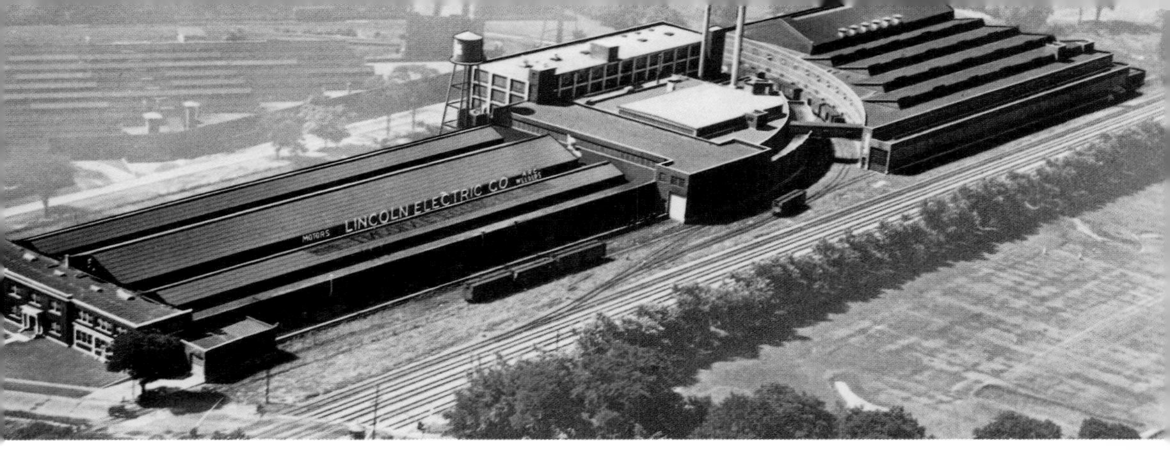

The Coit Road plant after three additions, 1940s.

had produced a cellulose-coated electrode prior to the A. O. Smith patent. According to Paul Jerabek, though the validity of the Cravens patent was questionable because of the poor welding characteristics of the electrode described in the patent, a clever lawyer and the technical ignorance of the judge enabled Lincoln Electric to win the suit in 1936.[9] This case soured the welding industry on patents, since patents enabled competitors to copy processes, more effectively protected when they were kept proprietary.[10]

Before the A. O. Smith patent suit was settled, Lincoln Electric surged well ahead of its competition. In the early 1930s the company had dominated the coated electrode business, since competitors were afraid to enter the market because of the contested patent. After 1934, sensing that A. O. Smith would lose the suit, competitors came out with their own brands of coated electrodes and Lincoln Electric's market share declined. At the time of World War II, however, Lincoln Electric still controlled about 50 percent of a rapidly expanding market.[11]

In the 1930s Jerabek hired two assistants, his brother Paul and his cousin, Ben Yukl, to assist him in his laboratory. They developed a stable of electrodes for welding different metals. These new electrodes made arc welding comparable or superior to the oxyacetylene process in almost every respect. By 1941 the company advertised between 30 and 40 different electrodes for specialized types of applications. T. E. Jerabek developed Hardweld, a high-carbon steel electrode with a dipped coating; Stainweld, an 18-8 stainless-steel electrode; Lightweld, for joining light-gauge sheet metal with a carbon arc; Toolweld, a high-speed steel-deposit electrode; Aluminweld®, for welding aluminum; and Manganweld, an austenitic manganese steel electrode for dipper teeth.

Members of the small experimental department applied Lincoln's credo of producing a quality product for more customers at a lower cost. They figured out how to use relatively inexpensive core wire to which they added alloys through the coating to achieve the properties they sought. In Paul Jerabek's words: "The trick was to design the product that would save the customer money." He developed Ferroweld®, a lower cost steel electrode for welding cast iron. He recalled the reaction of the research director of the largest electrode manufacturer in Norway who visited the factory shortly before World War II. The Norwegian was surprised to find out that Lincoln's experimental department consisted of no more than five men. Jerabek recalled: "He allowed that they also had five men in their lab, but Lincoln Electric Company made and sold more in one day than they did in a whole year!" The Norwegian remarked that his Swedish competitor, ESAB, had more than 40 engineers and 40 technicians in its laboratory.[12] Jerabek credited the astounding productivity of

Lincoln's experimental department to incentive management, but "it was not the money that was exciting," he emphasized. "It was the possibility of accomplishing something, creating something."[13]

It was difficult to sell welding machinery and motors during the Depression because manufacturers had little cash for capital improvements. However, they continued to need welding supplies. For Lincoln sales engineers, the Depression represented opportunity. They were selling a new method to join metals that would reduce manufacturing costs. "When business is moving," William Miskoe recalled, people in manufacturing have no time to think about innovations in the manufacturing processes, but "during slow periods they are willing to listen to a cost-cutting pitch."[14] To convince a prospect to buy a coated electrode that sold for 21 cents a pound instead of a bare wire electrode at 10 cents a pound, Miskoe insisted that it was not enough to give a dry, technical description of the cost benefits of coated electrodes. He always carried his gloves, welding helmet, and coveralls in his car when he called on prospects. "Now in welding," he emphasized, "it's always been said it can't be sold by talking. It's sold by showing."[15] He would volunteer to "weld one up" while the company president held his suit coat. The virtues of Fleetweld 5 – its ease and speed – generally clinched the sale.

Art Madson, Chief Instructor at the Lincoln Welding School, shows a student how to make a vertical weld, 1937.

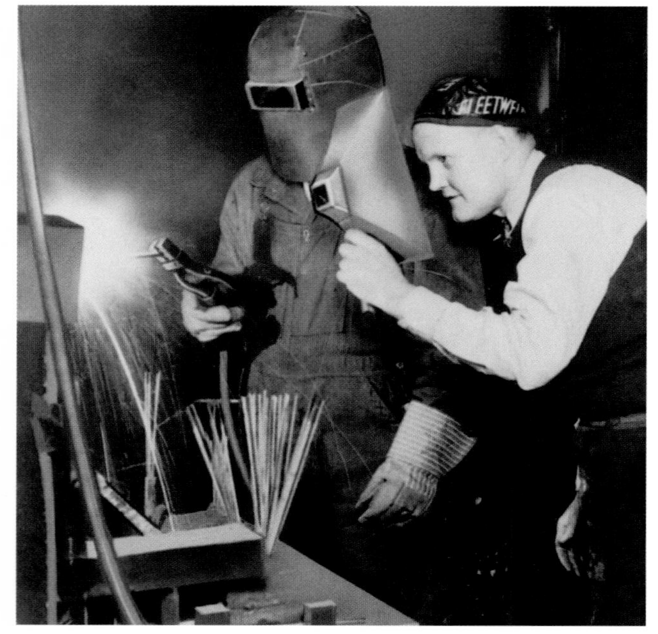

Particularly appealing to a prospective buyer were the cost savings that The Lincoln Electric Company guaranteed. A Lincoln sales engineer could promise that with Fleetweld one man could butt weld 40 feet per hour compared to 5 feet per hour using bare wire. After study of a manufacturer's operation, the engineer computed the savings the manufacturer could expect. The Lincoln Electric Company guaranteed to pay the difference if Fleetweld failed to live up to the expected cost savings. The Guaranteed

Cost Reduction Program, a distinctive Lincoln approach to sales during the Depression, continues to provide a compelling incentive to use The Lincoln Electric Company's products to reduce costs.

Fleetweld 5, introduced to welding operators through articles in the Stabilizer, rapidly won acceptance. Lincoln Electric's Welding School proved another venue for promoting loyalty to Lincoln's new coated electrode. In the 1930s welding students paid $15 for a four-week course taught by Arthur E. Madson, a towering man with a wide smile and steady hand. He inspired scores of students from all over the country to take pride in their welding technique. Because of the difficulty in holding a steady arc, Madson's approach was to grab the hand of the student. After striking the arc, he would guide the student's hand, slowly building confidence. Madson insisted they first master the art with a bare wire electrode since this required greater skill to lay down the bead. After this introduction, producing a smooth weld with the new coated electrode proved relatively easy. The welding school courses expanded the number of technically competent weldors and helped to break down the mystique surrounding arc welding.

THE BONUS: ANTIDOTE TO THE NEW DEAL

To Lincoln the New Deal was a "glorious larceny." He worried about the damaging effect of the new social programs on the country's economy and strongly disapproved of the millions of tax dollars spent on relief and social programs like the Works Progress Administration (WPA) created by Roosevelt to put people back to work. He thought the "government dole" robbed individuals of initiative. In June 1933, he confided his strong disapproval to his friend J. L. Morrill, then vice president of Ohio State University: "It would seem to me that what the White Father in Washington is doing at the present time would lead any right-thinking man to commit suicide or else drop his citizenship in this great and good Republic."[16] Morrill tactfully replied that at least Roosevelt was trying to do something about the country's problems. "Laissez-faire," Morrill wrote, "was the way people used to deal with typhoid fever and tuberculosis."[17]

The cure, in Lincoln's view, was worse than the disease. Lincoln often expressed adamant and outspoken opposition to the unhealthy and expensive bureaucracy the New Deal had created in letters to the editor of *The Plain Dealer* and the *Cleveland Press*. New Deal legislation boosted the confidence of organized labor. The most controversial section of the National Industrial Recovery Act concerned the right of employees to organize unions for the purpose of collective bargaining with employers. Collective bargaining gave unions the edge in the negotiation of wages and hours. Strikes broke out across the country. In Ohio it was estimated that about 25,000 workers joined ninety-six walkouts in 1933, about double the number of strikes in 1932.[18] Some companies in

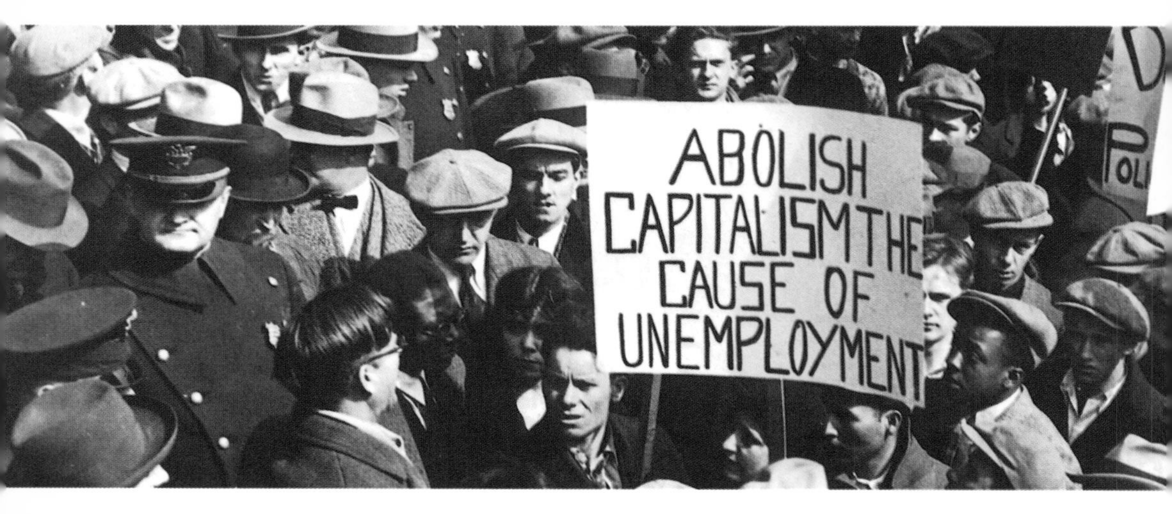

Cleveland vigorously opposed unions. Fred Crawford, president of Thompson Products (later TRW), for example, responded by supporting the creation of a company union. He fought the activity of "outside agitators" tooth and nail, taking them to court and appealing decisions when Thompson Products failed to win. Thompson Products succeeded in keeping national unions at bay, but at a high cost in time, money, and energy.[19]

Events leading up to the first Depression-era bonus are not entirely clear. In 1932 a decline in sales forced the company to reduce the number of hours employees worked. Nevertheless, hourly wages were not cut and no one was laid off. Lincoln posted an important notice on the factory bulletin board February 2, 1933, to acquaint his workers with the fact that they could expect a wage reduction when they returned to full-time work. This was necessary, he said, "to correspond more nearly with the rates of pay for the same sort of work in competing plants." Lincoln acknowledged that wage reductions were always objectionable to both employer and employee, but he asked his workers to accept them in "the same spirit" that management was demonstrating in not reducing wages immediately or laying people off.[20]

The following year after a complete reevaluation of all piecework rates, the company may, in fact, have reduced wages, since all base wage rates continue to be stated in 1934 "Lincoln dollars." To keep up with inflation after 1934, Lincoln introduced a company-wide adjustment multiplier. The multiplier is changed regularly and automatically in response to changes in the average hourly wage rate in manufacturing in the Cleveland area.

The 1934 reform of the pay structure set the stage set for the introduction the Lincoln bonus, an experiment that became the cornerstone of Lincoln's management philosophy. Lincoln always said that he decided to pay a bonus after a debate that took place in 1933 during an Advisory Board meeting. President Roosevelt's "more abundant life" speech is said to have prompted this debate. During this time of crisis, Roosevelt often promoted a "more abundant life" for workers, calling on business to assist in improving the standard of living of all Americans. Roosevelt believed that the New Deal's social programs would help make it possible for workers to have a share in the wealth

Unemployed workers demonstrate outside City Hall, 1930.
CLEVELAND PUBLIC LIBRARY

generated by capitalism. Lincoln took issue with Roosevelt's panacea. He approved of an abundant life, but not as an entitlement. Lincoln thought any money a worker received must be earned. A member of the Advisory Board is said to have asked him: "If we did more, tried harder and worked together as a real team, could the company pay us more?" Lincoln agreed that if his workers improved the efficiency of the company for a year, he would reward them. It seems the response of his workers to his first effort to pay a bonus in 1918 had disappointed him. It had been too small to make a real impression on them.[21] This time, he vowed, the bonus would be different.[22]

Lincoln kept his word. Without any fanfare, he posted a notice on the factory bulletin board asking the entire work force to assemble in the cafeteria on Saturday, December 22. Before passing out the bonus checks, Lincoln stood on a cafeteria table and gave a brief speech to "fellow workers." He emphasized that the bonus represented the improved efficiency of the company, achieved through their collective efforts. He also recognized special contributions of particular individuals. About 22 percent of the payroll that year went to workers' bonuses. Key management people, Clarence Taylor, Charlie Davis, George Landis, as well as Hal Kneen, the Factory Superintendent, T. E. Jerabek, and J. W. Meriam all received bonuses of $5,000 each.

Lincoln sternly warned employees not to discuss the amount of their bonuses (which averaged about $350 per employee) with each other and not to go home and boast about it to less fortunate neighbors. Lou Prebevsek, a worker in the wire room in Plant Number 2, remembered that he was standing next to a friend when they looked at their checks. His friend looked at the check and said, "$26! That's pretty good!" Prebevsek glanced over and declared: "That ain't $26. That's $260!" – a fact that rendered his friend speechless. Prebevsek

Lincoln Shield Arc Welders ready for shipment in the 1930s. This new model offered dual control to allow the operator to adjust the intensity of the arc.

recalled that Mr. Lincoln always admonished them to save their bonuses.[23] Lincoln thought the payment of a lump sum gave workers greater incentive to accumulate capital and provided them with the opportunity and desire to excel. Through their own efforts they could earn as much as a professional, make a large down payment on a house, send their children to college, and enjoy a higher standard of living than their parents.

The bonus had a tremendous psychological impact because it was paid in cash. Traditionally, Christmas bonuses, when workers at other companies received them at all, consisted of turkeys or other token gifts. Lincoln emphasized that the bonus that he distributed that day was not a gift. He later referred to it as an "incentive payment" that represented a sharing of the profits of the company earned through greater efficiency. In reflecting on that first bonus, he told the Navy Review Board in 1943 that he introduced it "tongue in cheek."[24] Clearly, it was a brave experiment and Lincoln did not know what to expect. Nevertheless, it should be pointed out that Lincoln instituted the bonus when the company, because of its strong sales in coated electrodes, could afford it. It may have been the *quid pro quo* for accepting a lower base wage rate when Lincoln reformed the wage structure.

Since Mr. Lincoln gave his workers a generous stake in the success of the company at a time of high unemployment, they had little motivation to press for changes in a system that worked for their collective benefit. Nevertheless, he took a hard-headed, down-to-earth approach to dealing with workers. For example, in a letter to the president of a small company beset with labor troubles he recommended setting up an Advisory Board like the one at Lincoln Electric. However, he warned him not to expect any gratitude for this action: "Never act as if you are doing the men a favor when you are doing it – put it on a strictly impersonal business basis and never be disappointed when your men turn on you when you least expect it just because human nature is that way, and don't expect to get credit for being fair or for being generous – employees turn on you in a minute when they feel it is to their advantage to do it and they are carried away with their own point of view."[25]

Lincoln believed the Wagner Act (allowing collective bargaining after the NIRA was declared unconstitutional) had turned labor and management into warring factions. Unions made workers class conscious, resigned to their low status and incomes. In Lincoln's view strikes weakened the economy, but the real losers in the struggle between labor and management were the consumers who had to pay a higher price for their manufactured goods. He wanted workers and management to join forces in promoting manufacturing efficiency to reduce prices, thereby raising the standard of living for all.[26] Lincoln took pains to make sure the Advisory Board was not construed as a company union. In April 1937 when members of the Advisory Board questioned whether the company was in compliance with the Wagner Act, Lincoln emphatically stated that the matter had been thoroughly

Lincoln's adamant opposition to the New Deal and his flair for public speaking made him sought after by radio hosts and meeting sponsors.

studied "and no change should be made or will be made as we comply with the regulations of that Act completely and thoroughly."[27] Operating without a union gave the company greater flexibility in shifting workers into areas where they were needed. For example, when a jump in sales of welders put pressure on production, the Advisory Board recommended that rather than hire new men, they ought to shift workers from the wire department into Plant Number One to work on the welder line.[28]

Lincoln's adamant opposition to the New Deal and his flair for public speaking made him sought after by radio hosts and meeting sponsors. The titles of his talks and pamphlets – "What Makes Workers Work?," "Incentives *vs.* Government Control," "Who Can Employ the Idle?" – summed up the simple message he drove home: Government interference in industry destroys the spirit of competition and drives out talent.

> Eventually we must find a way to eliminate the present tremendous economic waste represented by twelve million employable people who are out of work. We need what they can make. We are bowed down with the load of carrying them on relief and we are exasperated beyond words with the political poppycock that results from governmental handling of the problem...We must accept the fact that industrial employment and industrial production is not made by government but by the individual. All the comforts of life are not the result of governmental action (rather the reverse), but of the rare genius with an idea and with the moral, mental and physical attributes to put it through.

Why couldn't the New Dealers understand that it took a special kind of expertise to run a company? "There is nothing more involved, or more difficult, or requiring greater ability, than the successful management of a large industrial concern," he declared over radio station WGAR. "It requires the intelligence of a genius, the patience of a Job, the fighting ability of a Spartan, and the enthusiasm of a nut." In Lincoln's view, most companies failed because their leaders lacked these qualities.[30]

Shortly before the 1936 presidential election he wrote to Paul Bellamy, editor of *The Plain Dealer,* calling attention to "Mr. Roosevelt's failure as manager of the United States" who in his view had violated "nearly every plank of the platform on which he was elected and which he pledged his honor to uphold." He also chastised *The Plain Dealer* for its Democratic Party bias.[31] He urged John Lincoln to match his contribution of $25,000 to the Republican National Finance Committee. To James F. Lincoln, electing a new president was a patriotic duty. "If the present attitude in Washington continues this will not be a place where either you or I or our children can live with any degree of satisfaction."[32] In his efforts to defeat FDR, Lincoln was not alone. So strong was the opposition to the New Deal in Cleveland among the Republican establishment, especially members of the Cleveland Chamber of Commerce, that the city hosted the party's National Convention to nominate Alfred M. Landon for President.

EXPANSION ABROAD

Because J. F. Lincoln objected that under the New Deal, the government penalized businesses for creating new jobs, in 1938 he retaliated by refusing to invest another dollar on expansion in the United States. His anger precipitated a four-month world tour to look for investments abroad. At the invitation of Essington Lewis, the managing director of the Broken Hill Proprietary Steel Company (BHP), Lincoln toured Australia. He found the country rich in mineral resources, especially iron ore. It had no unemployment, and young men worked for wages two-thirds less than those in the United States.[33] Australia's rugged individualism and pioneer spirit appealed to Lincoln. He agreed that if Lewis could promise him 50 tons of steel a week, he would open a plant. Lincoln gave BHP 10 percent of the stock in the company in return for distribution of Lincoln's products through a British pipe company, partially owned by BHP. Lincoln bought a building in Sydney for 10,000 Australian pounds.

The Lincoln Electric Company (Australia) Proprietary Limited opened in 1938 with 15 employees, but its first two years were not auspicious. It had a bank debt of 5,000 Australian pounds, and owed Cleveland $30,000 for equipment and $25,000 for engineering and development expenses. The manager of the plant recommended shutting it down, but J. F. Lincoln was not ready to give up. In 1940 he asked William Miskoe, then branch sales manager of the Peoria, Illinois, office, to take charge of the Australian subsidiary. Miskoe, an engineer trained at the University of Virginia and the John Huntington Polytechnic Institute, had joined the company in 1933. Lincoln asked him to prepare for a job in sales by spending a year in the field learning welding techniques first-hand. Intelligence, integrity, and an outgoing personality made him an excellent salesman and sales manager. In asking him to take charge of the Australian subsidiary, Lincoln gave Miskoe an incentive of 10 percent interest in the company and a free hand in its management. Australia had strong unions, but Miskoe immediately set in place a modified Lincoln management system, including piecework, year-end bonus, and Advisory Board. The company's Advisory Board consisted of four representatives, elected by secret ballot from each of the four departments of the company, the works manager, and Managing Director Miskoe, who also served as chairman. Each member had a vote. Miskoe had a veto over the board's decisions, but he never exercised it.

Australian workers assemble Lincoln welding equipment, 1940s.

At first it was difficult to sell Lincoln electrodes because of Australian resistance to buying "Yankee" welding products, but World War II produced a demand for Lincoln products that continued into the postwar period. Miskoe made Lincoln Australia into a profitable subsidiary. He never had a strike and never had to lay anyone off. By 1946, his workers, the highest paid in Australia, opted out of their union. In a field dominated by tough British competitors, Miskoe's company had the highest output of finished product in Australia – three times that of its competitors. "Incentive management," he wrote in 1946, "is a new philosophy in industry, perhaps based on a true understanding of the worth of each who is employed in industry – shareholder, management, worker, and its obligation to the consumer. It is not the way to end immediately industrial strife, but it is a sound way, over a long number of years, to lead Australia to an industrial development that will be very spectacular."[34] In the 1950s after a disastrous fire, the company quickly built an entirely new factory. Miskoe reflected, "You can't have a union because a company that's unionized has two bosses pulling in the opposite direction...I wouldn't know how to run a company other than the way we do it here. You can look people square in the eye and say, 'This is right and that's why we're going to do it.'"[35]

Lincoln's subsidiary in Canada also avoided unions and could boast productivity about twice that of its competitors. The Lincoln Electric Company had purchased the controlling interest in 1932 from the Melvill Bertram family, who had founded the Canadian company with J. F. Lincoln in the 1920s.[36] In the late 1930s he asked one of his sales engineers, Michael K. Vuchnich, to take charge of the Canadian subsidiary. Early in his career Mr. Lincoln had singled out the former Ohio State football star for a leadership role in the company. He had sent Vuchnich off to the Bath Iron Works, one of the finest shipyards in the United States, to learn how to become an expert weldor. About 1936, when one of Armco's electrode manufacturing plants in South Africa started to founder, Lincoln sent Vuchnich to Johannesburg to show Armco how to run it. Vuchnich's success there put him in line for the Canada job.

Welding found a ready market in the late 1930s in Canada as the country industrialized and the steel industry grew. Vuchnich instituted incentive management and promoted arc welding with zeal characteristic of Mr. Lincoln. By December 1955 the Canadian company employed 150 workers, had sales of about $4.5 million and had paid a year-end bonus of about 30 percent of wages. The minutes of the Advisory Board contained the comment: "This has created a great deal of comment in Canada because it is something that no other manufacturer has ever done there."[37]

Although the manufacture of Lincoln electrodes in England went smoothly at first, the British venture proved a liability. The company bought an old factory in the early 1930s, then built a new factory in Welwyn Garden City in 1935. Lincoln placed George Clipsham in charge of his British operation. Because Lincoln strongly disapproved of the Labor government elected at the end of World War II, he sold the British company for $400,000 in 1947, including the Lincoln name, to George Clipsham, Robert E. Clipsham, and A. D. Marsh. At that time George Clipsham returned to Cleveland as assistant to the president and J. F. Lincoln began to look for a site on the Continent for manufacturing and marketing in Europe.

SPREADING WELDING KNOWLEDGE

Through the 1930s Charlie Davis and J. F. Lincoln repeated the company's mantra, "If it's steel weld it; if it's cast iron change it!"[38] To win acceptance for arc welding as a basic process, J. F. Lincoln formed strong personal relationships with metal fabricators whose decisions had an impact on design and construction. He became a friend of George Horton, president of the Chicago Bridge and Iron Company. This company became one of the pioneers in the industry in the application of arc welding, beginning in the late 1920s with the fabrication of tank bottoms. So successful was the introduction of welding with coated electrodes at Chicago Bridge and Iron that it was not long before the company abandoned riveting altogether.[39] Fleetweld 5 made it possible to weld all types of pressure vessels and dramatically influenced their design. For example, the popular "Hortonspheroids," fabricated by the thousands for storing oil, gas, and water, irrevocably changed the American landscape.

Welded design also proved the key to the success of R. G. LeTourneau, Inc., of Peoria, Illinois, an important manufacturer of earth-moving equipment, later sold to Westinghouse Air Brake Company (WABCO). In the early 1930s Lincoln convinced Robert Gilmore LeTourneau that welding could cut his manufacturing costs. To show LeTourneau exactly how to achieve Lincoln Electric's guaranteed cost reduction, Lincoln asked sales engineer William Miskoe to spend a year at LeTourneau's company. Welded bulldozers, scrapers, cranes, and rooters proved far stronger than equipment made of cast iron joined with rivets. The low cost, strength, and flexibility of welded steel construction enabled LeTourneau's company to grow exponentially between 1931 and 1938.[40] So successful was his experience with welded equipment that LeTourneau began to experiment

By the 1940s, arc-welded steel structures like these "Hortonspheroids" had altered the American industrial landscape.

with the construction of prefabricated steel housing for his workers in the 1930s. This led to the founding of Tournapull Housing Corporation in 1942.[41]

The most important application of Fleetweld 5, however, was in the construction of pipelines for the gas and oil industries. Again, J. F. Lincoln's personal relationships played a key role in advancing arc welding. Harold C. Price, founder of the Electra Welding Company (later H. C. Price, Inc). in Bartlesville, Oklahoma, specialized in repairing and building storage tanks using arc welding in the field. He failed in his attempt to weld a pipeline in 1922. Six years later he succeeded in welding a 169-mile pipeline for the Texas Pipe Line Company between San Augustine and Corsicana, Texas. For this job he used bare steel electrodes. In 1930, with J. F. Lincoln's assistance, he successfully welded a 32-mile gas line of 20-inch pipe for the Cities Service Pipeline Company using Lincoln's coated electrodes for the first time. Convinced that welds produced by Lincoln's coated electrode were superior, the following year, again with Lincoln's help, he bought new heavier Lincoln welding equipment, specially adapted for use with Fleetweld 5.[42]

Lincoln's friendship with Benjamin K. Smith also led to significant business for the Lincoln Electric Company. Born Benjamin Kopferschmidt, he founded the American Acetylene Welders Association in Jackson, Michigan, in 1917. Smith changed his name and founded Big Three Welding and Equipment Company in 1920 with two other weldors, C. K. Rickel and Charles Yoss. James F. Lincoln is reputed to have helped finance Big Three, the beginning of a long and profitable association between the two companies. At about the same time, Lincoln made a deal with Smith that if he could sell five welding machines a year he would give him the exclusive Lincoln distributorship for Texas, Louisiana, Oklahoma, and parts of Mexico. In 1926 Big Three, unable to find a contractor willing to weld a pipeline from Hodge to Monroe, Louisiana, decided to take it on as a Big Three project. The customer was a paper mill. Big Three used Lincoln's

Big Three Welding and Equipment Company's first pipeline, about 1926.

"Stable-arc" welding rod and welding equipment. Big Three's skyrocketing sales of both Lincoln Electric's welding rod and equipment, particularly after the introduction of Fleetweld 5, proved the wisdom of Smith's deal with Lincoln. His son recalled that although Big Three did not carry products of Lincoln Electric's competitors, it did sell oxyacetylene gas until 1934 when Lincoln told him to drop it from the product line. Benjamin Smith then organized the Smith Weld Company to carry the rival gas process.[43]

In addition to spreading knowledge of arc welding through the building of strong personal relationships, J. F. Lincoln relied on the written word. *The Procedure Handbook of Arc Welding Design and Practice,* first published in 1933, represented a landmark in this effort. This volume became the bible of the welding industry. It played an important role in winning a wider acceptance for arc welding among designers, construction engineers, and welding operators in the field. Still in print after many revisions, it has sold over a million and a half copies. During this period Charlie Davis endowed the A. F. Davis Welding Library at Ohio State University, at that time the world's largest collection devoted

Welding a joint on a 7-mile gas pipeline in northern Illinois using Fleetweld 5 electrodes, 1930s.

exclusively to welding. Davis also established awards for papers on mechanical and structural design and on maintenance and hardsurface welding for the American Welding Society.[44]

Although the perception of arc welding as a repair and maintenance tool had begun to change, J. F. Lincoln believed industry needed greater stimulus to abandon riveting and other traditional methods for joining metals. Convinced that the company needed an institutional base to communicate with the manufacturing and structural engineering communities, he established the James F. Lincoln Arc Welding Foundation with an initial donation from the company of $145,000 in 1935.

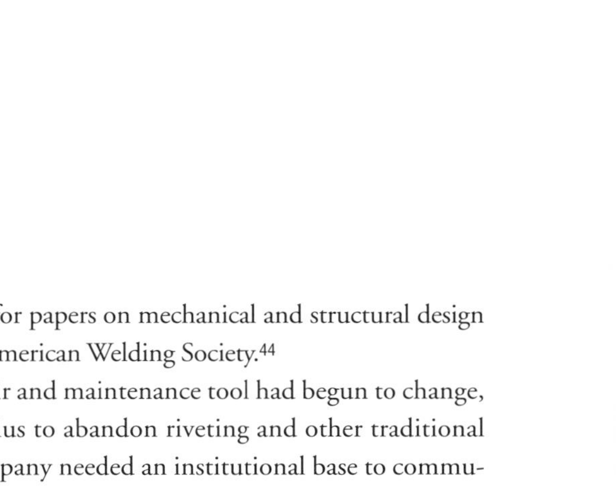

The foundation aggressively promoted arc welding through education. Its mission was to "encourage and stimulate scientific interest in, and scientific study, research and education in respect of, the development of the arc welding industry."[45] In contrast to the American Welding Society, which was a technical society, the foundation functioned as a trade association to promote the arc welding industry as a whole. The irrepressible Charlie Davis served as the foundation's first Secretary. Although financially supported by The Lincoln Electric Company through a yearly donation from the company, it continues to operate independently with a board of trustees composed of representatives from academia and the welding community.

Publications of the Lincoln Electric Company in the 1930s: "The Seven Keys to Welding Wisdom."

The foundation offered cash prizes for the best papers on subjects that explored new aspects of the application of arc welding. According to the rules, authors could describe how they had redesigned existing machines, structures, products, or parts to apply welding; or they could suggest how to design new welded products and structures or how to deliver new welding services. By the time of the first competition in 1936, the company had made an additional contribution to bring the total prize money to the princely sum of $200,000. The jury was made up of a distinguished group of engineering professors, headed by E. E. Dreese, chairman of the department of electrical engineering at Ohio State University.

The first competition, announced in February 1936, drew 1,981 submissions by the closing date of June 1, 1938. Some 445 contestants won prizes with the top paper receiving $13,700 – a small fortune during the Depression. Papers were divided according to an elaborate classification scheme, with 11 industrial classifications (automotive, aircraft, railroad, watercraft, structural, furniture and fixtures, commercial welding, containers, welderies, functional machinery, and industrial machinery) within which could be found 44 subject divisions. Maintenance and repair was conspicuously absent from the award categories.

The 1938 "grand award" went to A. E. Gibson and his wife, president and stockholder, respectively, of the Wellman Engineering Company of Cleveland for a paper entitled, "Commercial Weldery." Two British engineers won second prize with their paper, "The All-Welded Grid Applied to Plane and Spatial Structures." This pioneering paper in structural design was a precursor of the welded geodesic dome later made famous by Buckminster Fuller.

The foundation offered cash prizes for the best papers on subjects that explored new aspects of the application of arc welding.

Davis administered the Lincoln Foundation with his characteristic zest. The prize submissions represented new knowledge of arc welding applications and methods. He immediately produced condensed versions of the papers for popular periodicals and professional engineering journals. He assembled 109 of the most outstanding papers into a 1,409-page book, *Arc Welding in Design, Manufacture and Construction,* published in March 1939. The book sold for a mere $1.50 including postage, a bargain even in those days. Almost without exception, the papers stressed the cost savings involved when arc welding was adopted instead of rivets or cast iron. The use of weldments in the fabrication of airplanes, school buses, and locomotives required less metal than cast iron, thereby making these vehicles lighter, more streamlined, and less expensive to build. They were also cheaper to run because of lower fuel consumption.

The second award program, announced in January 1940, had a June 1942 deadline. Submissions reflected the new wartime applications for arc welding, though many could not be discussed because of military restrictions. Again the jury distributed $200,000 in prize money for papers on design, manufacture, and construction in the 11 industrial categories. Maintenance was included as an award category in recognition of the essential role it played as a repair tool both at home keeping the assembly lines moving, and on the field of battle.

Davis collected these papers into two books. The first, *Studies in Arc Welding,* included papers on ship construction, designs for anti-aircraft guns, aircraft hangars, armor-plate production, and the welding of armor plate for military tanks. It showed how arc-welded design and fabrication in defense industries could save hundreds of man-hours of skilled labor, conserve steel and other metals in short supply, and in some cases save lives. For example, because the seams of a welded tank were stronger, they usually could resist the force of an explosive charge that would rip apart a riveted tank. Welded joints of aircraft proved lighter and stronger and required less time than the laborious process of riveting. Welding proved a powerful tool for aircraft maintenance on distant airfields.

The second publication of the foundation, *Maintenance Arc Welding,* contained 25 papers that illuminated how repair of worn factory equipment had saved hundreds of tons of steel by making it unnecessary to fabricate new equipment. The foundation also prepared articles aimed at small repair shops. These shops expanded during the war because of the shortage of consumer goods and the need to keep old machines working. To repair broken parts of farm implements, tools, and vehicles quickly and cheaply, the mechanics in these shops needed to learn arc welding. At the same time,

Repair of a motor mount for a Douglas C-54 Army Transport, Oct. 1942.

More than any other period, the Great Depression shaped J. F. Lincoln's management philosophy.

Lincoln and Davis mounted a campaign to shape the thinking of the postwar generation. They wanted to teach students returning to school after the war to appreciate the future industrial significance of arc welding and focus on a career in the field. In 1942 they set up a 10-year series of undergraduate awards and scholarships for engineering students. The first Annual Engineering Undergraduate Award and Scholarship Program offered awards of $1,000 for the best papers on welded design. Scholarships carried an award of $1,750.

More than any other period, the Great Depression shaped J. F. Lincoln's management philosophy. By the end of the 1930s three of the four main elements of Lincoln Electric's incentive system were in place: the Advisory Board to promote dialogue between managers and workers; piecework to motivate workers to work faster and smarter; and the bonus to allow workers to share in the profits they helped to generate. By end of the decade J. F. Lincoln's promotion of arc welding through the James F. Lincoln Arc Welding Foundation had contributed significantly to the acceptance of arc welding as a basic technique in metal fabrication of all kinds. The foundation spread the gospel of arc welding into defense industries of all types, shipyards, small repair shops, technical high school programs, colleges, and engineering schools. Its system of cash awards reflected the principles of incentive management. Just as he had succeeded in tapping the creative energies of his workers by rewarding them for productivity, so also he stimulated the thinking of the engineering and business community by offering cash compensation for new applications. World War II would push J. F. Lincoln to justify Lincoln Electric's generous bonuses. Through his spirited defense of Lincoln's incentive system he would win a wider recognition for The Lincoln Electric Company.

[1] Carol Poh Miller and Robert A. Wheeler, *Cleveland: A Concise History* (Bloomington: Indiana University Press, 1997), 136.

[2] Arthur Todd, personal communication to the author, no date.

[3] "ESAB History," http://www.esab.com. Also, A. C. Nunes, Jr.," Arc Welding Origins," *Welding Journal* 55(1976): 571.

[4] See "Electric Welding," *The Engineer*, March 21, 1919, 267-269.

[5] A. O. Smith vs. Lincoln Electric, Brief for the Appellant, 13-14. James F. Lincoln Papers, Ms 3569, container 5, Western Reserve Historical Society, Cleveland, Ohio.

[6] On A.O. Smith's significance, see R.D. Simonson, 110-111.

[7] Special Welder Letter #15, Sept. 1, 1919. LEC archives.

[8] Interview with Louis Prebevsek, July 21, 1994.

[9] Interview and family history of Paul Jerabek, April 29, 1993. See also"Brief for Defendant"and"Brief for Plaintiff,"note 4, above.

[10] R.D. Simonson, 113.

[11] "Hearings before the Committee on Naval Affairs, House of Representatives, 77th Congress, Second Session. House Resolution 1962: A Resolution Authorizing and Directing an Investigation of the Naval Defense Program," Vol. 4, May 27, 1942, 908. James F. Lincoln Papers, Ms 3569, Container 6, Western Reserve Historical Society, Cleveland, Ohio. (Hereafter cited as "Hearings before the Committee on Naval Affairs.")

[12] Interview and family history of Paul Jerabek, April 29, 1993.

[13] Jerabek interview, April 29, 1993.

[14] Interview with William I. Miskoe, December 14, 1993.

[15] Interview with William Miskoe, October 5, 1992.

[16] James F. Lincoln to J. L. Morrill, June 20, 1933. Papers of Harry Carlson.

[17] J. L. Morrill to James F. Lincoln, July 7, 1933, Papers of Harry Carlson.

[18] Raymond Boryczka and Lorin Lee Cary, *No Strength without Union: An Illustrated History of Ohio Workers* (Columbus, OH: Ohio Historical Society, 1982), 193.

[19] See Sanford M. Jacoby, *Modern Manors: Welfare Capitalism since the New Deal* (Princeton: Princeton University Press, 1997), Chapter 5. For a somewhat less critical analysis, see Davis Dyer, TRW: *Pioneering Technology and Innovation since 1900* (Boston: Harvard Business School Press, 1998), Chapter 4.

[20] Notice, Feb. 2, 1933, in a file marked "Notices1933-1949," kept with the Advisory Board minutes which begin with the March 29, 1937, meeting.

[21] "Mr. Lincoln's Formula,"*Fortune*, Feb. 1944.

[22] Alton F. Davis, "James F. Lincoln Welds his Liberty Bell,"*Stabilizer* 17 (July, Aug., Sept. 1948), 3.

[23] Interview with Louis Prebevsek, July 21, 1994.

[24] Hearings before the Committee on Naval Affairs, 909.

[25] Letter from James F. Lincoln to H.L. Horning, President, Waukesha Motor Co., Waukesha, Wis., July 13, 1933. Papers of Harry Carlson.

[26] See various pamphlets written by Lincoln during this period, including "Who Can Employ the Idle?," "What Makes Workers Work?," "Tell the Truth and Keep Out of the Way." Also, *Lincoln's Incentive System* (New York: McGraw Hill, 1946).

[27] Minutes of the Advisory Board, April 28, 1937, LEC archives.

[28] Minutes of the Advisory Board, April 15, 1940.

[29] "Who Can Employ the Idle?"1930s pamphlet by J. F. Lincoln. LEC archives.

[30] James F. Lincoln, "What is on the Employer's Mind,"Jan. 9, 1938, over WGAR, LEC archives.

[31] Letter from James F. Lincoln to Paul Bellamy, Editor of the *Plain Dealer*, Oct 30, 1936. Papers of Harry Carlson.

[32] Letter from James F. Lincoln to John C. Lincoln, Feb. 12, 1936, Collection of Harry Carlson.

[33] *Cleveland Press*, May 12, 1938.

[34] "Address by Mr. W. I. Miskoe," *Proceedings of the First Australian One-Day Top Management Conference*, December 4, 1946, 90.

[35] David Whiteside, "Why this Obsolete Company is a Great Place to Work," *International Management*, April 1986, 51.

[36] On the purchase of the Canadian subsidiary, see Minutes of the Board of Directors, Oct. 3, 1932.

[37] Minutes of the Advisory Board, Dec. 27, 1955, LEC archives.

[38] *Stabilizer*, Feb., March 1936.

[39] *The Bridge Works: A History of Chicago Bridge & Iron Company* (Chicago: Mobium Press, 1987), 79 ff.

[40] "A Story of Faith that Led to Fortune," pamphlet published by the Lincoln Electric Company, c. 1938.

[41] See Meg Sondey, "An Initial Investigation of Welded Homes in the United States," unpublished paper presented at the 1990 Annual Meeting of the Society for the History of Technology, Cleveland, Ohio. A condensation of this paper was published in *The Welding Innovation Quarterly* 9 (1992): 4-7.

[42] "Highlights in the History and Development of the H. C. Price Company beginnings..." *Tie-In*, Winter 1956, 4-6.

[43] Telephone interview with Harry Smith, Oct. 4, 1994. Also, R. D. Simonson, 102.

[44] On the contents of the A. F. Davis library, see Robert S. Green, "Holdings in the A. F. Davis Welding Library," Engineering Experiment Station Circular no. 51. *Ohio State University Studies* 19 (1950).

[45] "History of the James F. Lincoln Foundation," typescript, c. 1978, LEC archives, 23.

J.F. Lincoln considers how to cope with the flood of orders for the company's improved Fleetweld electrodes during World War II.

Chapter 4

Incentive Management, 1941-1958

World War II created a tremendous demand for welding to build the ships, aircraft, and tanks needed to fight the war. Profits at Lincoln Electric soared. By the end of 1941 the company had net sales of $24 million compared to $13.6 million in 1940. Employees increased from 740 to 979. Through increased efficiency, sales value of products per employee went from $14,533 to $18,338.[1] The company produced almost half of the welding machines and consumables used by American industry and sold them for far lower prices than competitors. Demand for the popular Fleetweld 5 electrodes skyrocketed. Late in the war, sales of a granulated chemical flux for submerged arc welding, a process particularly suited to the welding of thick steel plate on Liberty ships, took off as well.

So strong were the orders for Lincoln products that sales managers were called back to Cleveland to assist in production. After large numbers of male workers were drafted, the company hired women factory workers who became expert weldors, learned to wind stators, and assemble. Men and women doing the same jobs received the same pay, although often jobs were restructured to make them physically less demanding. Reevaluation of these jobs resulted in a lower base rate for women. Women won their own representative on the Advisory Board, which by the end of the war had expanded from 14 to about 25 representatives.[2]

The Lincoln Welding School was hard pressed to keep up with the demand for arc welding operators. After training more than 20,000 men, the school accepted its first class of housewives, waitresses, and office workers in November 1942. When the women received their diplomas in January 1943, vice president Charlie Davis sent a telegram to the group: "By completing the class of welding you have demonstrated that you are entitled to stand beside the men in the Army and Navy and to say 'To

Hell with Hitler and Hirohito.' You are a fine example of American womanhood."[3] Women made good weldors because welding, unlike riveting, required manual dexterity rather than physical strength, and women, as it was often said during World War II, were "smart with their hands."[4]

The enormous increase in the number of trained weldors in the United States brought insecurity. Would thousands of operators be unemployed once the country returned to peace? Editorials in the company's *Stabilizer* magazine reassured readers. Charlie Davis wrote: "The National Defense Program with its demand for SPEED NOW is speeding the day when we'll really have ALL-OUT WELDING." He envisioned a time in the near future when "Manufacturers won't stop with brackets and bases... Bridge builders won't punch holes and fill them with rivets... Men will realize that the only way to get the ALL-OUT benefits of welded construction – strength, rigidity, light-weight, pleasing appearance, tight joints, [and] low costs – is to use welding ALL-OUT."[5] Through the *Stabilizer*, the company emphasized that the dramatic growth of arc welding from a repair process to "one of the biggest production processes in all industry" would create enormous demand for arc welding after the war. Among the applications envisioned were "all-welded stainless steel airplanes almost as numerous as today's cars... tear-drop shaped automobiles that have all-welded frames and bodies of low alloy steel... steel skyscrapers pushing skyward without the sound of a single riveter's hammer... insulated houses erected on one day of prefabricated arc welded block

Two former armature winders take positions as welding operators in the factory after graduation from the Lincoln Welding School during World War II.

sections." Rather than too many operators – an estimated 275,000 "behind the mask" in 1942 – there would be too few "when we begin to hum again on the products of a new age."[6]

The *Stabilizer* issued a call to action. Charlie Davis had always told operators, "The future of welding is in the operator's hands." Now he urged them not only to help win the war by producing "the best welded joints in the shortest possible time," but also to get active on the "study front" to prepare for the "Battle for Business" after the war. He recommended they spend 30 minutes per day on the *Procedure Handbook* and other Lincoln publications to improve their welding knowledge.[7] "The main thing is to keep our

Construction of a 300-foot freighter using Lincoln Shield-Arc Welders, March 1937.

Lincoln brandishes Fleetweld 5 electrodes during his defense of the bonus system, May 1942.

brain guns blazing away – to widen the breach in the ranks of Tradition and Laziness so we'll realize our objective of *more and better welding for more and better welders.*"[8]

LINCOLN'S SPIRITED DEFENSE

Wartime profits at Lincoln Electric swelled the bonus pool. In 1941 the four top managers of the company – vice presidents Clarence Taylor and Charlie Davis, chief engineer George Landis, and factory superintendent Hal Kneen (whose salaries ranged from $6,500 to $12,500) took home bonuses of between $40,000 and $50,000 each. Lincoln paid T. E. Jerabek, the shop foreman who developed Fleetweld, $25,000. One $35-a-week machinist pocketed a bonus of $3,000. In addition to paying out extraordinary bonuses, Lincoln set up a severance trust fund for workers because he was convinced the end of the war would bring a severe recession. He anticipated a precipitous decline in demand for the company's products. He set aside $1 million for severance allowances for 979 employees on the Lincoln Electric payroll at that time. The trust was irrevocable. Administered by J. F. Lincoln and two employees, it was to be completely paid out after ten years. In 1941 Lincoln also contributed $575,206 to the annuity he had set up for employees' pensions in 1936. The Lincoln bonuses and the severance and annuity funds seemed highly suspicious to government officials on the lookout for wartime profiteering.

In May 1942 the Navy's Price Review Board launched a formal investigation to find out whether the company's contracts needed Renegotiation. The Chairman of the hearing, Representative Carl Vinson of Georgia, called for a ceiling on the bonuses paid to officers and employees of the company. Edmund M. Toland, a lawyer famous for his aggressive cross-examination technique, presented the government's case. Toland insinuated that the company paid huge bonuses of between 60 percent and 100 percent of base pay, not only to evade corporate income taxes but also to keep unions at bay. He pointed out that if the company had paid federal taxes on its bonuses, the severance trust fund, and its annuity fund, it would have owed $8.8 million instead of $4.3 million for the years 1939-1941.

Toland called Clarence Taylor to the stand first. He demanded to know why Taylor deserved such a generous bonus. Taylor's answer revealed some of the reasons for the company's impressive earnings. He pointed out that the sales organization he had created sold about half of the welding machines and half of the welding electrodes in the United States. Its costs were about one-third

What he perceived as the government's determination to strip the company of its hard-earned profits outraged J.F. Lincoln.

those of tough competitors like General Electric, Westinghouse, Air Reduction, Linde, A. O. Smith, Harnischfeger, Hallop, Hobart, and Metal & Thermit. Asked whether the success of the company was due to the superior design of its machines, its sales organization, or the quality of its products, Taylor responded: "All of those things fit into the picture of a successful company. I don't see how we can break it down and say that this is due to the sales organization and this is due to engineering, any more than you can say that Joe DiMaggio is a successful batter because he holds his wrists a certain way."[9] In other words, The Lincoln Electric Company's application of a philosophy that permeated the entire organization accounted for its astounding profitability.

What he perceived as the government's determination to strip the company of its hard-earned profits outraged J. F. Lincoln. That afternoon after he called Lincoln to testify, Toland cut him off every time he tried to explain incentive management. Irritated rather than intimidated, Lincoln appealed directly to Chairman Vinson to allow him to address the committee. Permission granted, the gray-haired fifty-nine-year-old executive immediately jumped to his feet, pulling two electrodes out of his pocket. Now Toland had met his match. With what a reporter called "spell-binding eloquence" he justified the Lincoln bonus clearly and forcefully. Renegotiation, he argued, was comparable to the boss cutting the piecework price. It would destroy the incentive responsible for the impressive performance of his organization. Lincoln Electric's competitors, because they manufactured less efficiently, avoided Renegotiation. "No one else in the industry is going to be fined because the margin of profit with all the rest is very, very low, but because we have been efficient, we therefore – and only for that reason – are to be fined a large sum of money."[10]

Using a series of charts, Lincoln explained how by increasing efficiency, the company had been able to cut the cost of its products without sacrificing quality. He explained that between 1934 and 1942 sales of the company had grown by a multiple of six, from about $4 million to $24 million. Average workers' pay more than doubled over the decade while production per man-year more than quadrupled from $6,000 to $25,000. While the quality of electrodes had improved, electrodes that sold for 16 cents a pound in 1929 went for under 5 cents a pound in 1942. This price reduction reflected increased efficiency. It expressed Lincoln's goal of offering superior products to more and more customers at lower and lower prices. Lincoln argued that Renegotiation penalized the company for the exceptional efficiency it had achieved. Workers had earned these profits and the company had a right to reward them with generous bonuses.[11]

Lincoln's spirited defense of the company's bonus system began to garner favorable headlines in the national press, with articles like "How Much are Workers Worth?" in the *Saturday Evening Post* and "They Thanked Him for Coming" in *Nation's Business*.[12]

Cleveland newspapers, however, took a more jaundiced view. His old Democratic adversary, the Cleveland *Plain Dealer*, sarcastically noted that Lincoln Electric's generous bonuses made the abundant life promised by the New Deal seem more like a soup kitchen. "But the taxpayers, one fears, have taken the worst smacking, for it is, after all, their money which, indirectly at least, is financing Jim Lincoln's largesse."[13] The *Call & Post*, Cleveland's African-American newspaper, also took Lincoln to task, reporting in July 1942 that Lincoln did not believe black workers as willing "to master a skill" as their white counterparts. Lincoln had given in to the demand of white workers for separate toilet facilities, clearly in violation (along with a dozen other Cleveland firms engaged in war production) of President Roosevelt's Executive Order 8802 forbidding racial discrimination.[14] Preston Few, a retired African-American employee, recalled having quit over the issue of separate facilities during the war, but came back after the company had corrected the practice. He stayed at Lincoln Electric for 43 years, and was encouraged to move up in the company. He supervised the tool crib, served on the Advisory Board, and helped other African Americans win employment at Lincoln Electric. He was able to send his children to college and retire on savings invested in a string of apartment buildings.[15]

J.F. Lincoln hands out bonus checks to workers, 1946.

J. F. Lincoln's local image was also tarnished by a series of controversial letters he fired off to the editor of the *Cleveland Press* not long after he was elected president of the Cleveland Chamber of Commerce. He raised a furor when he suggested that the price of victory would be economic destruction of the United States. "Are we willing to pay the price of victory? If we are not, we had best change our attitude to that of living at peace with a Germany dominant in Europe and a Japan dominant in Asia."[16] The next day the *Press* called upon the Cleveland business community to repudiate their "defeatist" spokesman. Only one member did so publicly, and Lincoln rode out the storm. The following October *The Plain Dealer* featured a long article that enabled him to explain his views and laid to rest questions about Lincoln's patriotism. He declared that a war that resulted in annihilation of Germany and Japan would cost millions of Americans their lives. "War as a means of settling disputes must be outmoded or the world will commit suicide," he said.[17]

Lincoln's personality and his moral indignation left a deep impression on government officials.

Throughout the war J. F. Lincoln continued to defend his unique business philosophy, especially his right to reward workers with a bonus. In 1943, when the government threatened to withhold payments and to take away Lincoln Electric's priority access to scarce materials, he called it "bureaucratic terrorism" and refused to back down. He argued in a letter to James Forrestal, Undersecretary of the Navy, that the reduction in the selling price of Lincoln Electric's products had saved the government's war effort more than $200 million. For achieving this efficiency the company was being fined $3 million. "Our workers," he wrote, "because of the fact that they own the company and share in its profits, are producing at a rate of more than four times that of any of our competitors.... However, renegotiation recognizes profit only, not savings to the Government by efficiency. Hence the miraculous production of our men is penalized while [the] competition's lack of efficiency with its higher sales prices is not."[18] The force of Lincoln's personality and his moral indignation left a deep impression on government officials. An engineer who worked for the War Production Board recalled that he was told to cut off Lincoln Electric's supplies of aluminum, copper, and steel because the company was "stealing from the government." About 24 hours later he received a visit from five "towering" Lincoln representatives. They crowded into the bullpen that served as his office, determined to convince him that that it was none of the government's business how much Lincoln workers were paid. They argued, using a series of specially prepared charts, that The Lincoln Electric Company had demonstrated its ability to deliver a high-quality product for the lowest price. To cancel the company's priority rating was absurd. The country needed Lincoln Electric's production capacity. The government engineer recalled how, upon hearing an explanation of how the incentive system worked, he took the charts to his boss and "quickly convinced him we had made a mistake in canceling Lincoln's material allocation."[19] Deliveries immediately resumed.

Lincoln examines a welding specimin with T.E. Jerabek, the shop foreman who developed Fleetweld 5 and Chief Engineer George Landis (left), 1943.

Lincoln's problems with the government continued after the Internal Revenue Service stepped in to challenge not only the deductibility of workers' bonuses, but also the severance and annuity trust funds. The Treasury Department charged Lincoln Electric with tax evasion for 1940 and 1941, and levied a fine of $1.6 million. Investigators swarmed over the same company records already examined and photostated by the Navy investigators. "No man who works with his hands in a factory is worth $5,000 a year," one Treasury official is said to have declared. This statement became a banner headline and grist for Lincoln in his fight against what he called the "wrongheadedness" of the government. He thought every employee who contributed to the bottom line deserved a percentage of the profits of the company. The man who swept the factory floor was indeed worth $5,000 a year![20]

Meanwhile, the Roosevelt Administration was not yet through with Lincoln Electric. The Federal Trade Commission stepped in, this time charging that the company was selling below cost for the purpose of driving its competitors out of the business.[21] Lincoln responded that though the company had quadrupled its output, it was clearing less in profits because it had lowered prices. These lower prices saved taxpayers money. A survey by the Navy's Bureau of Ships proved the truth of the astounding efficiencies Lincoln Electric claimed to have achieved in its production of electrodes. The survey rated the 14 major producers of electrodes in the United States on the basis of the welding rod output per dollar of capital equipment. Lincoln scored highest with a score of 37. Its nearest competitor, Westinghouse, received a score of just 20. Of the 14 producers, Lincoln was the only company with a wire drawing operation at that time. The company's effort to automate, combined with the unmatched efficiency of Lincoln workers, enabled The Lincoln Electric Company to produce about two and one-half times more electrodes than the average for the industry.[22]

For Lincoln actions spoke louder than words. He volunteered to take a team of Lincoln technicians to visit competitors' plants to share Lincoln Electric's proprietary technology with them in order to increase their efficiency. According to a letter from R. E. Jones, Commander of the Bureau of Ships, to K. H. Rockey, Chairman of the Navy Price Adjustment Board, as a result of Lincoln's action national electrode production increased 33⅓ percent in the last quarter of 1942. By increasing the efficiency of existing plants the Navy saved an estimated $1.9 million that would have been needed for expansion of manufacturing facilities. Furthermore, to build these additional facilities would have required a delay of eight to twelve months before electrode production could be increased.[23] Lincoln explained this action to the company's board of directors by asserting his confidence that Lincoln Electric could keep its competitive advantage after the war because the company's competitors, even possessed of the latest technology, did not practice incentive management.[24]

J. F. Lincoln's public role in the defense of Lincoln Electric against Renegotiation had an impact on employees. He used Advisory Board meetings to explain the reasons for his actions and to influence their political views. For example, after Lincoln informed the Board that the company's refusal to be Renegotiated had "never happened before in all experience under the law." He called Renegotiation a threat to the stability of the country and urged his workers to write their congressmen.[25] The government's imposition of a fine of $1.6 million, he told the Board in 1944, threatened the bonus. If the company lost its appeal it might also "break the company itself." To defend the bonus Lincoln asked employees to write a justification of the "reasonableness" of their bonuses. He wanted them to explain "why you feel that you have earned more money than the Treasury Department feels should have been paid to you."[26]

Lincoln's stand on Renegotiation became controversial within the company. One young executive had the temerity to suggest that Mr. Lincoln was carrying his opposition too far.[27] But seeing this in a more positive light, another executive remarked that "J. F. Lincoln's colorful and courageous scrap on Renegotiation has been worth many thousands of dollars to the Company in increased public consciousness of our existence."[28]

Toward the end of the war, Lincoln began to think about the need to nurture future leaders of the company. He convinced the board of directors to adopt a plan to set up a junior board to give younger men in management a mechanism through which to communicate their ideas and viewpoints to the senior board of directors. The junior board functioned as a forum in which younger executives and senior management tested new ideas and developed a broader understanding of all areas of the company's operation.

The junior board was limited to ten members with J. F. Lincoln serving as an *ex officio* member. The board had representatives from the administrative division, including two each from sales, credit, cost, purchasing, accounting, office management, and advertising. One or more men were selected from engineering and development, a division that included application engineering, electrode development, automatic development, and welder development and design. Finally, Lincoln picked two management representatives from each of the two plants. This division included the production, employment, time study, tool and machinery design, and inspection departments. Junior board members served for one year and could be elected for an additional term of six months.[29] Members selected topics to research and report on to the group. The first policy they considered was whether the company should continue its focus on welding after the war. Mr. Lincoln revealed little patience for the idea of diluting the focus on welding by searching for new products to manufacture.[30] Indeed, one former member ruefully commented in an interview that though they prepared elaborate reports on various topics, Mr. Lincoln made decisions according to his own particular reasoning, regardless of the ideas and data they presented.[31]

Pushed into the limelight by the publicity surrounding the Navy hearings, Lincoln began to hone his management ideas.

Despite strong earnings during the war, Lincoln did not contemplate the return to peace with equanimity. He was convinced that the wartime boom had set the stage for a severe postwar recession. Again and again he urged his workers to save their bonus money in anticipation of leaner times. He pointed out the company faced a number of obligations and uncertainties including the specter of Renegotiation and the pending tax cases. In July 1943 the board of directors adopted Lincoln's recommendation to create a reserve of $4 million to be used to meet the challenges that the postwar economy would bring.[32]

Pushed into the limelight by the publicity surrounding the Navy hearings, Lincoln began to hone his management ideas. Up to this time Lincoln's writings had consisted of highly charged diatribes against the New Deal. Now they broadened into a more thoughtful philosophy of economic and social reform. He wrote: "Incentive management is more like a religious conversion. It is not a spur to the man to speed up; it is a philosophy of work. It is not a method of getting more work for less wages; it is a plan for making industry and all its parts more useful to mankind."[33] The publication of his first book, *Lincoln's Incentive System*, in 1946 enhanced his reputation as an industrialist with unique ideas on how to manage his workers. First published by McGraw Hill, *Lincoln's Incentive System* rapidly sold out the print run of 3,000 copies. The company bought the plates for the book and in two years sold an additional 100,000 copies for one dollar each. It was translated into French, German, and Japanese.

The fact that Lincoln Electric had the distinction of avoiding the strikes that swept industry shortly after the war as inflation reduced real wages seemed to lend credence to his theories. According to company lore, either during or after the war, a union organizer from the C.I.O. (Congress of Industrial Organizations) handed out leaflets inviting Lincoln employees to a noon meeting the next day in a small park across from the factory. As soon as he began his speech, a worker in the company parking lot began to test a large gasoline-driven generator whose muffler he happened to have removed. Unable to be heard above the din and subjected to the derisive laughter of the audience, the union organizer packed up. Management heard about the incident the next day.[34]

Lincoln never claimed to be against unions. In fact, he believed unions were necessary when management violated the Golden Rule. But workers who were treated with respect and rewarded for their contributions would have no interest in unions. In *Incentive Management* Lincoln wrote: "We know that if the worker is treated as a 'hand' by his boss, as a 'common man' by the politician, and as a 'union man' by many labor leaders, he will never develop his latent abilities. If a man is put into a class and becomes

Labor leader Harold Ruttenberg and Lincoln discuss Lincoln's new book, 1946.

class conscious, he thus becomes the same as his class and remains so. He will go to his grave a clod, even when he had the abilities of the genius latent in him."[35] Lincoln's book earned the admiration of Philip Murray, president of the C.I.O. and Harold J. Ruttenberg, the C.I.O.'s steel workers' research director. Ruttenberg and Lincoln sat down together for "a feast of reason" at the Lincoln plant in April 1946, shortly after the publication of *Lincoln's Incentive Management*. Said Ruttenberg, echoing one of the book's themes: "Men in factories have brain power that isn't utilized when they are treated as automatons. Treat them as human beings and you get more production."[36] Lincoln believed that a worker who was able to share some of the wealth generated by capitalism would feel no solidarity with trade unionism, communism, or socialism.

Lincoln's stature in the business community and the popularity of his book won him a place among the fifty "kings of business" selected by *Forbes* magazine in November 1947. The magazine had asked newspapers, businessmen, and Chambers of Commerce for nominations. Lincoln joined top executives like Charles E. Wilson, President of General Electric, Thomas Watson of IBM, and aircraft manufacturer Glenn L. Martin (once a Collinwood neighbor) for a special dinner at the Waldorf-Astoria. Pictures of all fifty businessmen appeared in *Life* magazine.

SCRUTINY BY HARVARD BUSINESS SCHOOL

The growing national prominence of J. F. Lincoln as a spokesman for profit sharing and the uniqueness of the management system he had conceived attracted the attention of management professionals. The prolonged study of Lincoln Electric by the Harvard Business School began with a report consisting of excerpts from articles in popular magazines, sections of the Lincoln Employee Handbook, and J. F. Lincoln's pamphlet, "Intelligent Selfishness and Manufacturing." It quoted a 1942 report in *Time* on Lincoln's wage incentives: "A $4,000-a-year-foreman got $25,000 extra; an $8,000 superintendent got $50,000 too. All told $4,071,315 was passed out in bonuses last year – nearly 10% of gross sales, and about 80% of net profits."[37] Was this too good to be true? In early 1946 two Harvard faculty members trekked to Cleveland to see for themselves. They produced an in-depth management study of The Lincoln Electric Company, published in 1947. This was the first of several case studies of the company's incentive system. For fifty years the merits of J. F. Lincoln's incentive system would be hotly debated by generations of Harvard Business School graduates.[38]

The 1947 case study relied heavily on an interview with J. F. Lincoln. What Lincoln stressed was that the bonus was earned, not handed out as an expression of goodwill on the part of management. Beyond the payment of a cash bonus, he explained, the system depended on the development of a

Lincoln workers designed their own posters to dramatize how the careless use of tools affected the bonus.

"frame of mind." Workers recognized that individual success and income were "inextricably bound to the efficiency and success of the company as a whole."[39]

J. F. Lincoln told the Harvard investigators that he had set as a goal a 10 percent reduction in direct-labor costs per year. They reported that he impressed upon workers the need to avoid unnecessary expenditures. For example, after a member of the Advisory Board suggested that the factory needed a public address system for announcements and piped-in music, Lincoln made sure that workers realized that the $50,000 price tag would come out of profits and ultimately each worker's bonus. The proposal was voted down.[40]

The Harvard study revealed other elements of Lincoln's evolving management system. For example, J. F. Lincoln opposed any capital expenditure that could not pay for itself in five years or less. (Later this was amended to one year, with exceptions up to three years.) This policy reflected not merely Lincoln's spartan attitude, but also his belief that it was not new technology, but creative ideas that made incentive management effective. The purchase of new machinery was not necessarily the most effective way to increase efficiency and lower costs. Lincoln Electric workers demonstrated their ability to adapt existing machine tools, often more than ten

Hal Kneen, factory superintendent (right), pays for his lunch while Charlie Davis (in shirtsleeves) reaches for a piece of pie. Blue collar and white collar employees still eat together in the Lincoln cafeteria.

years old, to run faster than the rated speed of new ones. They also designed their own jigs, fixtures, and tools.

An extensive interview with the plant superintendent, Hal Kneen, completed the picture of the early postwar factory. Kneen had graduated from Cornell University in engineering and started at Lincoln in 1929. Like Lincoln, he believed that one of the key elements in the success of company was the spirit of cooperation fostered by the Advisory Board. Its tradition of openness or "reciprocal frankness" allowed it to serve as an informal, yet inviolate, channel of communication between workers and management. A worker had the right to bring up any question without fear of retaliation. The Advisory Board also functioned, in Kneen's view, as a tool to educate workers in the principles of incentive management. They constantly heard Lincoln reiterate the need to reduce direct labor costs through reduction of waste and improvement in product design and methods of manufacture. The Board also functioned as a means of solving potentially divisive problems without direct intervention by management. For example, faced with an alarming increase in gambling during the lunch hour, J. F. Lincoln turned the problem over to the Advisory Board. Within a week, the workers had brought pressure on the offending gamblers to abandon this practice.[41]

According to Kneen, J. F. Lincoln's emphasis on fair dealing and honest treatment encouraged a sense of responsibility on the part of workers for the quality of their work. This resulted in the reduction of the number of inspectors needed in the plant. The Time Study and Methods Department's reputation for thoroughness and fairness and the knowledge that any worker could challenge a piecework price contributed to the atmosphere of trust between workers and management. Workers knew that the Methods Department could not change a piecework price merely to capitalize on increased productivity made possible by an individual worker's own efforts.

Finally, Kneen explained how the company's hiring practices contributed to the high quality of its work force. Factory workers were recruited with the same care as college graduates. Representatives of Lincoln Electric recruited shift workers from area high schools. They asked high school principals which students had both intelligence and leadership skills, often demonstrated through participation in team sports. The company also sought out graduates of technical and liberal arts colleges, presumably future leaders of the company, who were expected to begin on the assembly line or do clerical work until they had demonstrated their ability to become foremen or move up into office management. Through weekly meetings, foremen were kept fully informed of the company's problems and took direct responsibility for the operations of their departments, thus eliminating the need for middle managers who added to overhead.

In 1947 the authors of the Harvard case also sought out the opinion of a local labor leader who admitted he was convinced that any serious attempt to organize the workers at Lincoln Electric would prove futile. He observed: "They work like dogs at Lincoln, but it pays off." In his view, though few people could take the pace for very long, "there are plenty of people who are willing to burn themselves out for the kind of money Lincoln pays." He criticized what he felt was an overemphasis on monetary incentives. "If the day comes when they can't offer those big bonuses, or his people decide there's more to life than killing yourself making money, I predict the Lincoln Electric Company is in for trouble."[42]

REFINING THE INCENTIVE SYSTEM

Lincoln Electric's bonus reflected J. F. Lincoln's thinking about how the profits of a business should be divided. Of the various stakeholders of a business, the customer should come first, employees second, and stockholders third. Lincoln believed the close relationship between efficiency and profitability made workers the most important stakeholders in the business. He wrote in *A New Approach to Industrial Economics* that customer satisfaction depended on producing a quality product at an affordable price. "In doing that, the most important person from a cost standpoint is the worker. He alone can make the product of a quality and at a price that will please that customer. He must be rewarded for this and rewarded in proportion as he accomplishes the purpose."[43] The bonus, Lincoln emphasized, was an "extra reward" over and above regular wages.

Lincoln thought workers' compensation more important than dividends to stockholders. Though stockholders deserved a reward for risking their capital, they were not entitled to dividends of more than 6 percent on the net value of the company. Dividends, he wrote in 1951, should be "somewhat more than the return from safe investment in high grade bonds and somewhat more

In 1948 J. F. Lincoln began to recognize individuals at the bonus ceremony who had made important contributions to the company with additional cash awards.

than average dividend rates." After deduction of dividends and "seed money" for future capital needs, the balance should go to the workers.[44] The board of directors and the Lincoln family (who owned the majority of the stock of the company) stood firmly behind this principle. The board determined the amount of the annual bonus distribution, called the "bonus pool." There was no formula. The bonus pool varied from year to year.

In the early years, to determine employees' individual bonuses, J. F. Lincoln simply met with his secretary each Thanksgiving and assigned a bonus amount after the name of each employee, based on the number of years with the company, wages, and his personal assessment of each worker's contributions. In 1947 the company instituted a more formal merit rating plan, probably in response to the Internal Revenue Service's insistence that there should be a more objective method of determining the bonus. The merit rating plan assumed the average employee would earn 100 points. An employee might score either above or below 100, but each department or group of small departments had to average 100. The averaging requirement prevented inflation of scores. Each supervisor rated his or her workers on four characteristics, each worth twenty-five points: output, quality, supervision needed, and cooperation and ideas. In special cases, a supervisor was permitted to issue evaluations over 120 points. (In the late 1960s this was changed to 110 points.) The points of these exceptional employees did not count in the group's 100-point average. The amount of each bonus was arrived at by multiplying a worker's wages by the merit rating (taken as a percentage) times the "multiplier" (the percentage of the gross bonus determined for that year by the board of directors). Each year the announcement of the "multiplier" was the climax of the December bonus ceremony.

In 1948 J. F. Lincoln began to recognize individuals at the bonus ceremony who had made important contributions to the company with additional cash awards. Arthur Todd, manager of the Traffic Department, was the first to be honored as "Man of the Year" for succeeding in getting freight rates reduced by $500,000 a year.[45] J. F. Lincoln never took a bonus himself. His executives and a handful of outstanding employees received a bonus, but did not receive the merit rating. This group met after the bonus ceremony in Mr. Lincoln's office where he presented checks representing his personal assessment of each of their contributions to the company that year.

In the 1950s J. F. Lincoln instituted the final key element of his incentive system: guaranteed continuous employment. He believed workers who feared layoffs would distrust management.

Their fear would prevent them from giving their full attention to increasing efficiency. "If we follow the philosophy of Christ as given in the Sermon on the Mount," he wrote in 1961 in *A New Approach to Industrial Economics*, "we shall have the proper answer to the problem of lay-offs. When we treat the worker as we would like to be treated, the answer is plain. Continuous employment is needed to secure the cooperation of the worker. It is also basically sound."[46] He considered layoffs a bad habit – "an escape mechanism for the ineffective manager."[47] Security changed workers' attitudes toward their jobs. It unleashed their latent creativity.

To the end of his life J. F. Lincoln continued to believe that the principles of incentive management reflected basic truths about human nature.

Although guaranteed continuous employment was always implicit in Lincoln's attitudes and actions toward workers, he took great care in gradually making it a formal company policy. In 1949 Lincoln tried to avoid layoffs during a steel shortage by reducing the number of hours some employees worked to 30 hours a week. They had to agree to accept whatever work was available, but they kept their jobs. Smaller bonuses in 1949 reflected this economic downturn. In January 1951 Lincoln instituted a plan for guaranteed continuous employment on a trial basis with a posted notice that acknowledged that it was "an experiment that poses many problems."[48] Suddenly faced with a heavy demand for electrodes and welding equipment during the Korean War, he resisted hiring new workers who might have to be laid off when the inevitable retrenchment occurred. He thought in the long run the new policy would increase the incomes of everyone at Lincoln Electric, but he warned that strikes by suppliers, material shortages, or accidents might temporarily have an effect on the bonus.[49] Lincoln counted on the flexibility and dedication of his workers. In Lincoln's view, guaranteed continuous employment would promote a positive attitude toward the job and make employees willing to take additional overtime during boom periods. He was not disappointed. Likewise, he expected employees to accept a four-day workweek and accept any job within their capabilities during slack periods. When transfer to less demanding jobs in many cases resulted in lower earnings, the Advisory Board debated how to compensate for lost wages. It was decided that such transfers would be recognized in the bonus rating as evidence of cooperation.[50]

Lincoln thought the new policy of guaranteed employment would also stimulate the ingenuity of members of management because it was their job to make sure employees had work to do even during economic downturns. "Management should plan for slumps as a normal occurrence," he wrote. "They are useful if properly used."[51] Slack periods pushed management to find ways to develop new products and methods of manufacture and to explore new markets. In 1958 after seven years of trial, Lincoln Electric's Guaranteed Continuous Employment Plan became the established policy of the company. Each year the board of directors votes whether it should be continued. Since 1949 there have been no layoffs at The Lincoln Electric Company.

To the end of his life J. F. Lincoln continued to believe that the principles of incentive management reflected basic truths about human nature. And he never lost his enthusiasm for spreading the Lincoln Electric message to other companies, assuring them that by implementing incentive management they would cut their costs at least in half and bring them dominance over their competitors. "Expect that your company will write a new chapter in industry," he wrote. "Do not be satisfied with less. If you do not get such results, you have failed to understand and apply incentive management."[52]

However, some students of the system questioned whether incentive management was an ideal to be emulated. How democratic was it, anyway? The philosopher Erich Fromm devoted several pages to the Lincoln system in his discussion of capitalism in *The Sane Society*, published in 1955. Fromm called Lincoln's version of profit sharing "super-capitalism." By encouraging competition and teamwork and paying generous bonuses, employees reaped the benefits of capitalism and wanted no part of unions. Fromm thought Lincoln stockholders probably received less than their due from the system. He also pointed out that the system did not empower workers. "In spite of the talk about the 'human person' everything," he wrote, "the rating of the work as well as the amount of the worker's bonus and of the dividends, is determined by the management in an autocratic fashion."[53]

Be that as it may, employees took great pride in their employment at Lincoln Electric and how the cash bonus had transformed their lives by enabling them to accumulate substantial personal savings and to invest in their futures. An article in *Reader's Digest* called "A Factory Full of Partners" gave examples of factory workers who had retired on their savings. Nellie Griffiths had worked as a die-lapper (polishing dies) for twenty years. She returned to her native Ireland with enough money to buy an estate with a ten-bedroom mansion, greenhouses, a conservatory, boathouses, and stables. She had enough money left over to turn it into a resort. Other employees had invested in real estate or retired to travel around the world. People at Lincoln worked hard. The *Digest* article pointed out that the work environment included neither coffee breaks nor piped-in music. "The unheard melody playing there is the distant jingle of the Christmas bonus."[54]

[1] James F. Lincoln, *Incentive Management* (Cleveland: The Lincoln Electric Company, 1951), appendix, 262.

[2] Advisory Board Minutes, July 27, 1943.

[3] *Stabilizer*, Jan. 1943.

[4] *Atlanta Constitution*, Jan. 13, 1942.

[5] Charlie Davis, "Let's Prepare for All-Out Welding," April/May 1941, 2.

[6] J. L. Morrill, "Weld Wanderings," *Stabilizer*, Aug./Sept. 1942, 2.

[7] Charlie Davis, "You're in the Army Now–On Two Fronts!, *Stabilizer*, Oct./Nov. 1941, 2.

[8] Charlie Davis, "The Breach is Widening–Let's Keep Our Guns Blazing,"*Stabilizer*, Nov./Dec. 1941, 2.

[9] "Verbatim Record of Proceedings of Committee on Naval Affairs of the House of Representatives Investigating the National Defense Program," Wed. May 27, 1942, published by the Bureau of National Affairs, Inc., 715. James F. Lincoln Papers, Ms. 3569, container 6, Western Reserve Historical Society, Cleveland, Ohio.

[10] "Verbatim Record,"685.

[11] See Hearings before the Committee on Naval Affairs, House of Representatives 77th Congress Second Session. Vol. 4, May 27, 1942, 909-10. James F. Lincoln Papers, MS 3569, container 6. Western Reserve Historical Society, Cleveland, Ohio. Also "Mr. Lincoln's Formula," *Fortune*, Feb. 1944.

[12] Fred R. Barton, "They Thanked Him for Coming," reprinted from August, 1942 *Nation's Business*, "How Much Are Workers Worth?," *Saturday Evening Post*, July 24, 1943. LEC archives.

[13] "Four with One Stone," Editorial, *Plain Dealer*, May 29, 1942.

[14] *Call & Post*, July 11, 1942. Both Warner & Swasey and Thompson Products were prosecuted for racial discrimination during the war. See Christopher Wye, "Black Civil Rights," in David D. Van Tassel and John J. Grabowski, eds. *Cleveland: A Tradition of Reform* (Kent: Kent State University Press, 1986), 125.

[15] Interview with Preston Few, Feb. 11, 1993.

[16]"Letter to the Editor,"*Cleveland Press*, Aug. 5, 1942. Editorial, "Mr. Lincoln Goes Defeatist,"*Cleveland Press*, Aug. 6, 1942.

[17]"Louis Birnbaum, "J. F. Lincoln Answers Critics; Speaks up on War,"*Plain Dealer*, Oct. 18, 1942.

[18] Congressional Record, Appendix Oct. 27, 1943, A 4880. James F. Lincoln Papers, Ms 3569, Container 6 , Western Reserve Historical Society, Cleveland, Ohio.

[19] Interview with Bart Fagan by Richard Sabo, Oct. 27, 1992.

[20] See "Mr. Lincoln's Formula,"*Fortune*, February 1956. In 1946, the Tax Court held against Lincoln Electric on the annuity and severance trust funds. Lincoln fought this case for ten years. The court originally ruled that the trust was not tax deductible because a single lump-sum payment did not constitute a profit-sharing plan. After two appeals, this dispute ended in 1952 with a decision in the company's favor. The Tax Court of the United States, *The Lincoln Electric Company, Petitioner, v. Commissioner of Internal Revenue*, Respondent, Docket no. 1296, Promulgated March 26, 1952. Papers of James F. Lincoln, Ms 3569, container 6, Western Reserve Historical Society, Cleveland, Ohio.

[21] J. F. Lincoln, *Lincoln's Incentive System* (New York: McGraw Hill, 1946), 85.

[22] R. E. Jones, Commander Bureau of Ships, to K. H. Rockey, Chairman, Navy Price Adjustment Board, March 20, 1943. Letter appended to LEC Board Minutes of the Shareholders' Meeting, April 28, 1943, vol. 3, 76.

[23] R. E. Jones Letter March 20, 1943.

[24] Shareholders Meeting, April 28, 1943, Board Minutes, vol. 3, 76.

[25] Minutes of the Advisory Board, Oct. 4, 1943. LEC archives.

[26] Minutes of the Advisory Board, Nov. 6, 1944. LEC archives.

[27] Minutes of the Junior Board, Oct. 13, 1943. LEC archives.

[28] Minutes of the Junior Board, Feb. 2, 1944. LEC archives.

[29] Records of the Junior Board of Directors. Original constitution, Oct. 20, 1943. A list of all reports from 1943 has been kept, but prior to 1951 most reports are missing.

[30] Minutes of the Junior Board, Feb. 2, 1944.

[31] Arthur Todd, informal communication with author, Oct. 1992.

[32] Minutes of the Board of Directors, July 9, 1943, vol. 3, 86. LEC archives.

[33] J. F. Lincoln, *Lincoln's Incentive System* (New York: McGraw Hill, 1946), 160.

[34] Fred B. Barton, "They Thanked Him for Coming,"Nation's Business, August, 1942. James F. Lincoln, "Labor Efficiency as Viewed by Top Management," *Proceedings of the Personnel Institute*, Ohio State University, May 12, 1943, 77.

[35] James F. Lincoln, *Incentive Management: A New Approach to Human Relationships in Industry and Business* (Cleveland: The Lincoln Electric Company, 1951), 35.

[36] *Plain Dealer*, April 18, 1946.

[37] "The Lincoln Electric Company, HB 277, Harvard Business School [1947].

[38] "Observations on the Lincoln Electric Company," Case Study EA-A 42, Harvard Business School, 1947. See also, "The Lincoln Electric Company,"HP 227, Harvard Business School, [1946].

[39] "Observations on the Lincoln Electric Company,"Case Study EA-A, 1947, Harvard Business School, 2-3.

[40] Case Study EA-A, 3-4.

[41] Case Study EA-A, 5-9.

[42] Case Study EA-A, 10.

[43] James F. Lincoln, *A New Approach to Industrial Economics* (New York: Devin-Adair Company, 1961), 117-18.

[44] James F. Lincoln, *Incentive Management* (Cleveland: The Lincoln Electric Company, 1951), 110-11.

[45] Arthur Todd, personal communication to author, about Oct. 1992.

[46] James F. Lincoln, *A New Approach*, 88.

[47] James F. Lincoln, *A New Approach*, 80.

[48] Announcement appended to Advisory Board Minutes, Jan. 16, 1951.

[49] Announcement.

[50] Advisory Board Minutes, June 15, 1954.

[51] *A New Approach*, 86.

[52] James F. Lincoln, *Incentive Management* (Cleveland: The Lincoln Electric Company, 1951), 119.

[53] Erich Fromm, *The Sane Society* (New York: Reinhard & Company, Inc., 1955), 240-46.

[54] Blake Clarke, "A Factory Full of Partners," *Reader's Digest* reprint, 1962. LEC archives.

Chapter 5

Manufacturing a Few Things Well, 1945-1965

JAMES F. LINCOLN OFTEN REPEATED HIS CONVICTION that his company conducted its business on a set of principles that were radically different from other companies. The Lincoln Electric Company did not follow business management fads. He celebrated the company's unique management system and never missed an opportunity to assert that government subsidies, funded out of the pocket of the producer, killed initiative. His distrust of the New Deal's legacy prompted him to keep a copy of the U.S. Constitution on the wall of his office "as a memory and for a hope."[1] After reading a 1953 *Plain Dealer* editorial cautiously advocating public housing, Lincoln fired off a letter to the editor in which he wrote: "You cannot reward the incompetent from the winner's winnings and have a lasting nation."[2]

"You cannot reward the incompetent from the winner's winnings and have a lasting nation." –J. F. Lincoln

A Cleveland reporter, who visited Lincoln in his rather modest, windowless office in 1954, found Lincoln, then approaching 71, "still young in everything but years."[3] He described him as an imposing man, "as impressive as the great plant created out of his own energy, ability, and intellectual brilliance." The location of the chairman's office, deep within the factory, seemed to symbolize Lincoln's decision to operate his company differently from other businesses of the period. "J. F. Lincoln, in this citadel, is shielded by a Lincolnian moat from an industrial world he thinks runs on a wasteful, non-incentive policy, from an economic world where workers aren't doing a tenth of what they could (and possibly should) be doing, and from a political world which he finds filled with too much government."[4]

Lincoln believed in manufacturing "a few things well, rather than many things not so well."[5] He promoted the idea of vertical integration through the elimination of the middleman in the purchase of raw materials. He wanted the company to be able to buy raw materials as far back in the supply

George A. Bryant, president of the Austin Company (center, bending forward), presents a model of the new 20-acre plant to Lincoln executives.

chain as possible. That effort took capital. The company made large investments in calcining, crushing, and sizing equipment. For some rare ores Arthur Todd, then head of purchasing, went directly to the mine. Lincoln made it a rule that in purchasing it was forbidden to commit the company to materials or services beyond a year. Todd recalled that he once broke the one-year rule and bought two and a half years' supply of rutile ore for a terrific bargain. Lincoln insisted he sell the extra 18 months' supply to a major broker. He later bought it back at a net loss to Lincoln of about $375,000. Todd remarked: "I thought then and now that this was a matter of preferring policy over common sense. Needless to say, the ore broker became my friend for life."[6]

J. F. Lincoln's emphasis on streamlining manufacturing, combined with his fiscal conservatism, made it difficult to introduce anything new. Stick electrodes and DC arc welding equipment continued to be the mainstays of the company's product line. Lincoln did not encourage new product development because it involved risk. Money that went into R&D cut into profits and reduced the year-end bonus. Resistance to new ideas became endemic in the company. Arthur Todd remarked, "Selling Lincoln [Electric] on doing something new has never been anything but an arduous and discouraging task."[7] An engineer wrote on the bottom of a memo to Leonard Giles, in charge of hiring, "Every time I mention a suggestion to J. F. he gives me the devil."[8]

Idealarc, a transformer/rectifier type welder, could be operated on either AC or DC welding current.

Despite J. F. Lincoln's general philosophy to leave new product development to competitors, there were exceptions to this rule in the 1950s. The company developed agglomerated flux for submerged arc welding, an enormously successful product developed in response to a competitor's patent infringement suit. Another important development involved Innershield®, J. F. Lincoln's answer to the threat posed by the increasing popularity of gas-shielded arc welding. The company introduced Idealarc®, a transformer/rectifier welder with dual arc control to produce either AC or DC welding current, and brought back three-phase electric motors to the product line. If J. F. Lincoln resisted change during this period, he brilliantly succeeded in keeping the company focused on manufacturing a few things well. Through the halcyon years of the 1950s Lincoln Electric continued to pass on to customers lower costs made possible through efficient manufacturing.

POSTWAR BATTLES

After the war the company tangled for fifteen years over a patent infringement case brought by the Linde Division of Union Carbide and Carbon Corporation against Lincoln Electric and its customer, Graver Tank & Manufacturing Company. Submerged arc welding was vastly superior to manual welding with bare or coated electrodes for many applications. It produced no blinding glare from the arc. The electric arc was submerged or hidden underneath a dry, granular substance called "flux" that consisted of chemicals that protected the weld from the atmosphere. The submerged arc process produced a strong, smooth weld without the smoke and spatter of manual welding. Thick steel plates, particularly important in ship building, could be welded in a single pass. Called an "automatic" welding process, a steel wire was fed continuously through a wire feeder at the same time the flux was applied. The flux and wire fused with the "parent," or base metal, creating a molten pool of steel covered by melted chemicals. The method's drawback was that it required that the work piece be held in a horizontal position, often requiring a large capital investment in lifting equipment.[9] Both Linde and Lincoln Electric developed automatic welding equipment in the 1930s that was sold along with coiled wire electrodes and flux. Lincoln Electric's "Hidden Arc" process was the result of collaboration with R. G. LeTourneau. A special nozzle patented by the Caterpillar Tractor Company helped speed up the process. This patent was sold to Lincoln Electric.[10]

In a famous patent case against Lincoln Electric, Linde claimed that the "Unionmelt" process, patented in 1936 by the Linde Air Products Company, was an invention, because (unlike other automatic processes) it produced no arc. Linde argued that Lincoln's "Lincolnweld" process, introduced in 1945, infringed on its patent. Lincoln's lawyers contended that both processes were identical and were

Welding the grid for a new upper deck roadway for the Brooklyn Bridge, 1964.

a direct extension of the automatic weld process invented by Boris Robinoff in 1930.[11]

A 1947 opinion by Indiana District Judge Luther M. Swygert threw out 17 of Linde's process claims. He agreed with Lincoln Electric's lawyers that an arc (though hidden or submerged) was produced. Therefore, the process was not new. However, he ruled in favor of Linde in four out of seven fused-flux claims. An appeal to the United States Supreme Court in 1949 upheld these flux claims, forcing Lincoln to withdraw its 660 flux from the market. This spurred the development of a new chemical formula for flux by L. Keever Stringham, an engineer who gave distinguished service to the company. Stringham had graduated from Cornell in 1933 when Paul Lincoln was dean of the engineering school. He heard J. F. Lincoln speak at a meeting of the Cornell chapter of the American Institute of Electrical Engineers (AIEE) and used the occasion to line up a job. Stringham developed a new flux called Agglomerated 770™ for submerged arc welding after the court ruled in favor of Linde. This flux consisted of fine particles mixed with silicate and fired in a kiln.[12]

After years of litigation over the Linde patent case, in a final appeal in 1960 the court reduced damages from $3.25 million to a little less than $1 million.[13] Lincoln regarded the case as a victory for free enterprise against Linde's effort to establish a patent monopoly. "Patents should not be used as an umbrella to ward off competition and prevent low selling prices," Lincoln told reporters upon announcing the company's victory in the suit.[14] In fact, The Lincoln Electric Company reaped long-term benefits of patent protection for Agglomerated 770 flux. The 770 flux later captured 80 percent of the market and helped Armco International, Lincoln's world distributor until the mid-1980s, prosper in the postwar period.

Another postwar battle that J. F. Lincoln waged with characteristic zeal was over the restrictive engineering standards applied to welding. These standards and test requirements prevented the arc welding industry from passing on lower costs to customers. Lincoln produced a barrage of articles promoting arc welding between 1944 and the early 1950s specifically targeted at engineers and architects who continued to design structures without recognizing the special merits and design requirements of welding. He used these articles to argue that requirements for x-rays and other tests were holding back acceptance of the process. Lincoln pointed out in a letter to the *Scientific American* that welding mild steel produced welds that were actually stronger than the parent metal, yet these welded joints needed to be tested while riveted joints were not subject to any tests at all: "While a welding electrode is tested in every conceivable and nonsensical way, no one suggests any test on a rivet, yet the riveted joint is always the weakest spot in any structure."[15] When the *Scientific American* editors invited representatives of the bolt, nut and rivet industry to reply to Lincoln's challenge, they declined. Their silence seemed to lend credence to Lincoln's position. An article by Lincoln in the *Welding Journal* several years later again asked for new welding standards and the elimination of unessential testing. Lincoln claimed the welded joint, made of carefully selected steel, had to be tested, while the parent metal, usually manufactured to a lower standard, had no such requirements.[16] Arc welding would prevail definitively over riveting only after the physics and chemistry of the weld were fully understood.

STREAMLINING PRODUCTION

Efficiency increased dramatically at Lincoln Electric after 1951 when the company moved from the cramped Coit Road plant to a carefully designed new factory in Euclid, Ohio. The new plant reflected J. F. Lincoln's faith in the latent abilities of Lincoln workers to find ways to reduce costs. At the entrance to the new plant he placed an epigram attributed to the nineteenth-century French poet, historian, and statesman, Alphonse de Lamartine: "The actual is limited, the possible is immense."

William Irrgang, who succeeded Lincoln in 1965 as chairman and CEO, best expressed what Lincoln meant by bringing out an individual's latent creativity. He had left his mark on the design of production equipment in the electrode division. Born in Germany in 1907, Irrgang had graduated in 1928 from the State Technical School in Cologne with a degree in electrical engineering. Runaway inflation in Germany influenced his decision to look for work abroad. Although he knew only the rudiments of English, he booked passage to the United States. He found a job at Westinghouse in Pittsburgh. Fearing a layoff and hearing they were hiring at Lincoln Electric in Cleveland, he applied for work at the Coit Road plant. He started on the assembly line in the motor division as an armature winder. His technical creativity soon brought him to Lincoln's attention.

By drawing its own wire, the company could control the quality of the steel used in electrode manufacture.

In 1938 Irrgang developed a new high-speed unit to draw, straighten and cut steel wire for the manufacture of welding electrodes. By drawing its own wire, the company could control the quality of the steel used in electrode manufacture. Even more important, this allowed the company to reduce the cost of wire from the $17 a ton it cost competitors (who continued to buy drawn wire from their steel suppliers) to $1 a ton.[17] It was this new wire drawing technology that J. F. Lincoln shared with competitors during World War II. In recognition of Irrgang's extraordinary contributions to semi-automating electrode manufacture, Lincoln named him director of plant engineering in 1946.

Between 1946 and 1949 preparing the new factory layout preoccupied Irrgang. He enlisted George Willis, one of the company's rising stars, to help plan the new assembly lines. Willis had graduated from Michigan State in June 1942 with a B.S. in chemical engineering and a minor in metallurgy. After active duty as an Army officer during World War II, he had won a place in the first postwar class to attend Harvard Business School. (The class that year had 35,000 returning veterans vying for 370 places.) Willis's class was the first to study the Harvard case on The Lincoln Electric Company. In class he debated how Lincoln's system compared with the Cleveland-based automotive and aircraft parts manufacturer, Jack & Heintz. Jack & Heintz used lavish perks like all-expenses-paid honeymoons and country club memberships to encourage productivity. Which system would succeed? Willis staked his future on J. F. Lincoln's more compelling principles of incentive management. He remembered how upon arriving at the plant for an interview, Lincoln took him through the plant, then asked him what he had seen. Willis replied, "The work rate is extraordinary but the plant is a big job shop with no apparent logical materials flow and too much materials handling." Lincoln hired him on the spot.[18]

Willis and Irrgang agreed that materials handling costs in the Coit Road factory were disproportionately high when compared to direct labor costs. This disparity – a tribute to the ingenuity of Lincoln workers who continually found ways to streamline manufacturing – needed correction. To plan assembly lines for the new plant, it was necessary to rethink how a finished machine was produced by taking it apart step by step along a reverse assembly line. One of the engineers involved in setting up the new lines described the process: "Starting with the completed machine, parts were removed from the machine as it was moved back along an imaginary assembly line. The removed parts

The new "factory in a warehouse" concept (top) eliminated the central storeroom and allowed parts to be stored at the point of use where the worker would keep visual control of the inventory.

Manufacturing took place at the point of assembly (middle). In the center a worker welds while another inspects large engine-driven welders.

Overhead conveyors (left, bottom) moved material efficiently from one station to another. Subassembly shop at right allows the worker to set his own pace.

were allocated a storage area along the assembly line where they came off. We thus arrived at an ideal straight line operation."[19] While maintaining production, the new assembly lines were tested to discover how to achieve maximum efficiency. They used the old plant as a proving ground for full-scale standard production runs. Workers at every skill level were encouraged to make suggestions.

The new $8.5 million facility on St. Clair Avenue in Euclid was built by the Austin Company, a pioneer in the design of the straight-line, "controlled conditions plant." The controlled conditions plant had developed in the early 1930s hand in hand with welded structures.[20] In collaboration with the Austin Company, Lincoln engineers designed a manufacturing space that was both functional and flexible. A writer for the magazine *Steel* observed: "First and foremost, the new building aims at further reduction of costs. Every feature of its design is motivated by ways and means to pare indirect costs and give workers more productive time, less lost motion. There are no unnecessaries."[21] Newspaper accounts referred to it as a "factory in a warehouse" to emphasize how the new design contributed to cutting indirect labor costs in manufacturing by eliminating the central stockroom, a traditional feature in factory design.

The long rectangular factory building actually contained two completely autonomous plants: Plant Number One to manufacture welding machines, and Plant Number Two for stick electrodes, coiled wire and flux for submerged arc welding. The entire structure was without windows and had few columns to impede the flow of materials. With 80 percent more floor space than the Coit Road plant, the added dimensions of the new factory allowed all materials to be stored at the point of use. This new arrangement reinforced the principles of incentive management, since workers now had the additional responsibility of keeping visual track of inventory. Minimizing the number of times that materials needed to be transported through the plant also cut down on paperwork. The reduction in labor costs allowed the company to transfer thirty-four workers from the stockroom into direct production.

The change from a functional arrangement to one of straight-line production made it possible to keep equipment tooled up on the floor so that little time was lost in changing set-ups. Some of the machinery of the former winding and punch press departments, for example, could be integrated into the new assembly lines. Subassemblies located adjacent to the line in which they were to be used allowed them to be fabricated as needed. The piecework system gave workers the freedom to control the pace of work to produce the number of subassemblies required for each day's run.

The change from a functional arrangement to one of straight-line production made it possible to keep equipment tooled up on the floor so that little time was lost in changing set-ups.

Materials and parts were unloaded, inspected, and distributed from the north end of the plant. The plant had higher than normal clearance under the roof trusses so that an integrated system of overhead cranes with a transfer crane system for moving materials from bay to bay could be installed. This elevated transport system meant that aisles could be narrower. The plant's high ceilings allowed materials to be stacked as high as 17 feet. Fork-lift trucks removed finished product from conveyor belts at the south end of the plant. Workers in shipping, who had previously hand-loaded welding machines weighing 150 to 4,000 pounds, used a specially designed hairpin hook with a built-in hoist to lift and lower heavy machinery into trucks for shipping.[22]

The piecework system gave workers the freedom to control the pace of work to produce the number of subassemblies required for each day's run.

Visitors, employees, and executives all entered the building through a long subterranean tunnel that went under a plant rail spur and the perimeter truck roadway to the center of the plant where it joined another tunnel that ran the entire length of the plant. Executive offices were located in an internal two-story building constructed between the two plants. To reach the factory floor, workers used one of twenty stairways to bring them within 200 feet of each work station. Located along this tunnel, away from the factory floor, were workers' locker rooms, rest rooms and the distribution system for power, water, compressed air, and natural gas. The cafeteria, also located along the tunnel level, epitomized J. F. Lincoln's no-frills philosophy. It had multiple purposes, serving as a meeting and conference room when meals were not being served, as well as the company auditorium. There was (and is) no executive dining room. Large meetings, such as the bonus distribution, continue to be held in this space.

Changes in the layout of the electrode manufacturing plant were less dramatic, since Irrgang had already succeeded in streamlining the process. Both the processes for making flux for submerged arc welding and for stick electrodes was then, and is today, highly automated with few workers. They have physically demanding jobs that command high gang piecework rates. Lincoln plant engineers custom-designed most of the machinery in the electrode division. It was built, maintained, and repaired on site. After the move William Irrgang focused on perfecting the technology of the electrode dryer to make it jam proof – an effort that took six years and three prototypes to get right.[23]

Just before the move, Lincoln promoted George Willis to head of the electrode division, one of the key jobs in the company. Willis supervised the move of the division's huge extruders, dryers, mixers, and kiln. Great care was taken in planning the move. Since piecework output is reflected not only in daily earnings, but also in the year-end bonus, no one wanted to lose valuable production time during the move. With the help of local movers, Lincoln workers moved 1,500 machines and hundreds of tons of materials in twenty working days. During this time production never dropped more than 10 percent.[24] Workers kept a minimum of seven extruders running throughout the move.

In the 1950s when the plant was completed, the new design of the receiving dock at the north end facilitated the unloading, analysis, and classification of between fifteen and twenty tons of steel per hour. (Today in the same plant, workers handle fifty tons per hour.) The design also permitted bulk raw materials like flourspar, magnesite, iron ore, and manganese ore to be transported directly into the plant in trucks or railroad cars.

SALES AND ENGINEERING TALENT

At six-feet five-inches tall, the dynamic Wallace R. "Buck" Persons headed the Lincoln sales organization. Persons, a 1932 graduate of the Case School of Applied Science in civil engineering, had begun his twenty-year stint at Lincoln as a sales trainee in 1934. He moved on to run the Pittsburgh District Office, and then returned to Cleveland, eventually to serve as vice president of sales and marketing and one of the company's directors. Persons took the conversion to peacetime welding sales in stride. True, some contractors still used riveting, but he was confident the James F. Lincoln Arc Welding Foundation would provide them with the necessary design knowledge and know-how to make the transition to welding. In a report, Persons wrote: "As mentioned above 'business will not be dull' in our industry for several years, first because we are still *growing*, and secondly because welding equipment actually *costs nothing*! It is one of the few types of products which earns its sale price in a short time and continues to earn for 10 to 15 years."[25] Between 1947 and 1949 the production of welding equipment exceeded sales by 25 percent, allowing the company to gradually reduce its backlog. In 1949 Persons predicted increased sales of welding equipment into the foreseeable future.

Persons based his optimism on the anticipation of both replacement sales and reaching out to new customers as the industry grew. He noted that hundreds of old welding machines needed to be traded in for improved equipment. Persons encouraged his salesmen to make a survey of the old machines in service in their districts and to offer trade-ins. These machines were then "Linc-Conditioned" at the plant and resold to small repair shops at bargain prices. Through the *Stabilizer*, the Lincoln newsletter circulated to weldors, the company encouraged returning servicemen, trained as weldors during the war, to set up their own welding businesses. These entrepreneurs, it was hoped, would contribute to expanding the postwar welding industry.

To sell new welding equipment, Lincoln salesmen asked customers to use new machines on a trial basis, since this almost always resulted in a sale. When companies could not afford the capital investment in a new machine, they could rent it with an option to buy. Salesmen gave shop demonstrations and stressed that the company's new 200-ampere AC unit had 60 percent more capacity than most competitors' machines and sold for $35 less. Persons projected that the capacity of the new Euclid plant would allow the company to keep machines in stock, even with the anticipated increase in sales.

To tap the farm market, Lincoln salesmen taught classes in welding to high school students through the Future Farmers of America.

The farm market required a new approach to sales.

Buck Persons also saw a potential mass market in the three million farms in the United States. Niels C. Miller, founder of Miller Electric, was the pioneer in this field. In the mid-1930s he introduced a high-frequency alternating-current transformer-type welder specially designed for farm use.[26] Lincoln Electric would prove an able competitor in this market, working through 4-H Clubs and high school shop classes. By 1948 Lincoln Electric had introduced a new welder with a special "Arc Booster" to accommodate rural power lines. The company also manufactured small DC welders powered by an air-cooled engine, and "Selfweld," which utilized a special stand to make welding easier for less experienced weldors. In a special film for farmers, the new Lincoln welding equipment was pitched as an "extra hand" to make timely repairs. It showed a farmer's wife striking her first arc and laying down a welding bead. "Why that was easier than my first seam on a sewing machine!" she enthusiastically declared on camera.

The farm market required a new approach to sales. Dealers were given a choice of whether they wanted to be industrial or farm dealers. Industrial dealers continued to receive a 10 percent discount on welders and accessories and to be supervised by Lincoln branch offices. Farm dealers received a 20 percent discount on non-industrial machinery and dealt directly with the factory.

When L. Keever Stringham, inventor of agglomerated flux, became chief engineer of the electrode division in 1951, he applied Lincoln's management principles. In Stringham's view communication between the engineers in design and those in production was the key to creating a successful product. He thought it made no sense to design something and then have the manufacturing engineers object: "We can't afford to manufacture that."[27] He made sure that all the engineers working on a specific product worked in close enough physical proximity to encourage a healthy give-and-take.

Stringham and Lincoln often locked horns over the issue of new product development. Because Lincoln believed in keeping the product line small, he insisted that for every new product developed, one had to be removed. In the mid-1950s Westinghouse and General Electric, following Miller Electric's lead, developed advanced AC transformer-type welders. These welders were easier to use and permitted higher electric currents. It was clear that the old motor-generator set the Lincoln Electric had been manufacturing since the 1920s was inefficient, noisy, and expensive to make. Along with John Murray, later chief engineer in charge of machine development, Stringham implored Lincoln to let them develop a transformer-type welder. As late as 1957 this effort was opposed by Irrgang, who was reluctant to enter "a strange field which would require new skills, and that we would be merely attempting to catch up with competition, rather than offering any new method or procedures to the process."[28]

Jerry Hinkel recalled asking why they needed to develop a welding machine that could provide either AC or DC welding current. It seemed to him that it was a two-headed calf. Why not just an AC transformer? "Stringham called me aside. How the hell are we going to get AC welding machines out of this plant if we don't take this tiny step to get into it?"[29] "Idealarc" had selenium rectifiers and proved a worthy addition to Lincoln's arc welding product line.

Stringham always congratulated himself on the decision to hire Robert Shutt, another individual whose latent abilities were tapped by Lincoln Electric's incentive system. Shutt had an unusual background. Generally the company hired only electrical, mechanical, and metallurgical engineers. They all started on the shop floor as piecework operators and won their promotions as they demonstrated their ability. Bob Shutt did not fit this profile. In 1950 he had graduated magna cum laude from Kenyon College in Gambier, Ohio. His degree was in physics, not engineering. L. K. Stringham recalled that Shutt was so persistent when he interviewed at Lincoln Electric that he "beat me down and took a job away from me."[30]

Jetweld, an iron powder electrode, increased the ease and speed of welding and eliminated spatter.

As a young man Shutt won recognition for the development of Jetweld®, an iron powder electrode that revolutionized welding because of its speed, appearance and the ease with which weldors could learn to use it. Because the coating melted rapidly, welding speeds and deposition rates could be increased without using high electrical currents that often caused too much penetration, gouging of the parent metal, and spatter.[31] Jetweld had many of the advantages of a low hydrogen electrode and could be used for low-alloy steels, high-sulfur, free-machining and medium-to-high-carbon steels. Shutt recalled that few at Lincoln knew about the development of Jetweld until his boss, L. K. Stringham, asked him to demonstrate it in front of the both J. F. and John C. Lincoln. The founder, then in his eighties, was still a good judge of arc welding breakthroughs. Shutt received a patent in 1953.[32]

Shutt's new iron powder electrode enjoyed phenomenal sales while competitors like General Electric, Air Reduction and Murex scrambled to develop their own versions of the new electrode. Jack S. Roscoe, vice president of sales, declared in 1956, "Our men are having a field day with the powdered metal electrode business as Jetweld is pretty much in a class by itself and our sales of this electrode have been going up consistently every month since we introduced it. The end is not yet in sight, and it should not be because there is a lot of green pasture yet to be taken over."[33]

Shutt's new iron powder electrode enjoyed phenomenal sales while competitors like General Electric, Air Reduction and Murex scrambled to develop their own versions of the new electrode.

Lincoln asked his son-in-law, Howard Morris, to develop a cost-effective method to manufacture iron powder, a major constituent not only in Jetweld, but also in other iron powder manual electrodes that were later developed. He succeeded in creating a unique process by which iron ore could be converted into high-grade iron powder using continuous direct reduction in a rotating kiln. In 1956 he was recognized as "Man of the Year" for this achievement. His citation noted that the expected savings in the first year would be in excess of $200,000.

Shutt also discovered how to make important improvements in the company's staple, Fleetweld 5. It was given the new name of Fleetweld 5-P. Of the approximately one hundred different electrodes produced by the electrode division, Fleetweld 5-P produced the greatest profits for the company for more than thirty years.

Although J. F. Lincoln had attracted a cadre of extremely talented and motivated individuals, in the 1950s it became clear to a number of them, including Persons and Stringham, that J. F. Lincoln was determined to maintain his control over decision-making at all levels of the company. He was intent on keeping the company small, with a limited product line, focused on its core business. Individuals who found Lincoln's business philosophy unpalatable, or their opportunities for advancement limited, left the company. In 1954 Buck Persons moved to St. Louis to take over as head the Emerson Electric Company. He transformed Emerson from a relatively small St. Louis

Through the 1950s The Lincoln Electric Company concentrated on manufacturing a few products with maximum efficiency.

company with two factories and annual sales of $50 million to a large, diversified corporation with more than 18 factories and $900 million in sales.[34] Later Stringham, Richard B. Loynd, and Charles O. Planting followed Persons into executive positions at Emerson Electric. "Buck and I both left Lincoln," Stringham explained in a 1987 interview, "because J. F. Lincoln was never going to give up running that company."[35] Indeed, until the year of his death in 1965, James Finney Lincoln maintained absolute authority over all the company's operations and decisions.

DOING THE IMPOSSIBLE

Through the 1950s The Lincoln Electric Company concentrated on manufacturing a few products with maximum efficiency. Meanwhile, the welding industry underwent a radical shift. Gas-shielded arc welding, a small niche market prior to the war, began to gain in popularity. Because it is a continuous process, it greatly enhances the ease of welding. Gas-shielded arc welding produces less spatter and smoke than manual welding with stick electrodes. Since the gas is delivered through the same gun as the wire, it requires only a bare steel wire electrode fed continuously through a mechanical wire feeder. Thus it is faster since it is not necessary to stop welding each time an electrode has to be changed, and more efficient because operators can use higher electric currents without the problems associated with the breakdown and embrittlement of coatings. Gas-shielded arc welding also offers a versatile alternative to submerged arc welding because it is not necessary to hold the work piece in a horizontal position.

Gas-shielded arc welding gained in popularity during World War II for welding a range of different metals. Welding operators used a helium gas and a tungsten electrode to weld the highly reactive metals aluminum and magnesium. After 1948 success with the tungsten inert-gas (TIG) process contributed to the development of the metal-inert-gas (MIG) process for welding aluminum, stainless and mild steels. When carbon dioxide gas as a shielding agent was introduced, its low cost pushed the acceptance of gas-shielded arc welding. The only drawback of gas-shielded arc welding was in the field – atop a skyscraper, for example – where wind tended to blow away some of the gas.[36]

Despite the growing popularity of the new process, the use of gas in welding remained as much of an anathema to J. F. Lincoln as it had been in the years after World War I when arc welding had competed with the rival oxyacetylene process. Lincoln was reluctant to enter the gas-shielded business because he doubted that it would ever prove profitable. Competitors such as Linde, Air Products, Airco, and Chemetron, as well as European companies like Air Liquide of France, Messer Griesheim of Germany, and the British Oxygen Company all manufactured gas, and Lincoln did not want to help Lincoln Electric's competitors by selling their product. He emphasized that Lincoln Electric's profits came through the efficiency of its manufacturing processes. He disapproved of buying industrial gases from outside suppliers because no value could be added to the product. He viewed the sale of steel wire for the gas-shielded process with the same fierce opposition. Although at this time Lincoln Electric sold steel wire, along with Agglomerated 770 flux, for submerged arc welding, this wire comprised only a small percentage of sales. Lincoln feared if gas-shielded arc welding became popular, eventually the large quantities of wire it would require would prompt steel manufacturers to sell wire directly to end users.[37]

As the market for gas-shielded welding began to expand in the early 1950s, J. F. Lincoln looked for an automatic or semi-automatic process that would preserve the flexibility of all-position manual welding without the use of externally supplied gas shielding. George Landis, vice president of engineering, began to experiment with the idea of placing the shielding ingredients that protect the weld from the harmful effects of the atmosphere inside a tubular wire electrode. The attraction of placing the flux within the wire was that it could be coiled and fed continuously through the welding gun.

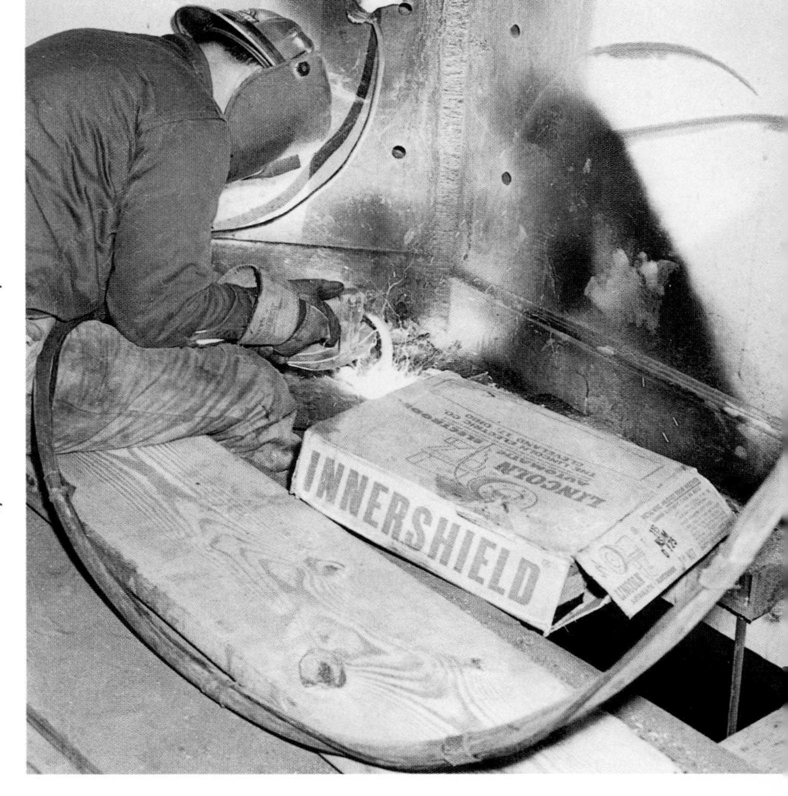

Innershield required no gas or flux. It produced a dense vapor shield around the arc to protect the weld pool from the atmosphere.

Interestingly, John C. Lincoln had anticipated this idea in his patent for a tubular "flux holder" in 1929.[38] Landis predicted that placing the flux within the wire would permit higher electric currents accompanied by increased deposition rates. For large industrial jobs where the increased speed of welding could dramatically reduce costs, the new continuous process promised to be revolutionary.

The development of the electrode that came to be called "Innershield®" was J. F. Lincoln's strategic response to the increasing popularity of gas-shielded arc welding. Innershield had the kind of common-sense logic that appealed to J. F. Lincoln – just turn a conventional stick electrode inside out and place the flux inside a continuous tubular steel electrode. Both Lincoln and William Irrgang strongly believed in the future of Innershield. Both underestimated the difficulties of developing and manufacturing this product, so simple in concept but devilishly complicated in its chemistry and physics. The development of Innershield presented extraordinary scientific, engineering, manufacturing, and marketing challenges. It affected every division of the company for over twenty years. As no product before or since, it tested Lincoln's "team spirit" and proved that Lincoln's management philosophy could motivate employees to achieve a seemingly impossible technical breakthrough. But it also revealed J. F. Lincoln's growing inflexibility and Irrgang's uncritical devotion to his mentor's ideas.

As no product before or since, it tested Lincoln's "team spirit" and proved that Lincoln's management philosophy could motivate employees to achieve a seemingly impossible technical breakthrough.

The development of Innershield put the career of Robert Shutt, future vice president of engineering in the electrode division, on the line. Shutt had the daunting task of developing Innershield from a prototype into a marketable product under the watchful eye of William Irrgang, then president of the company. Irrgang gave him an unlimited budget and required a daily report. Shutt faced Irrgang each morning with trepidation. "He would strip your hide off, if you didn't know what you were talking about," Shutt recalled, but Irrgang was also the best engineer and "the most compassionate person I ever knew." To Shutt, the physicist, it seemed as though he was being asked to do the impossible. He recalled: "From everything they told me, it seemed as though they wanted

Making a fillet weld with a Lincoln Squirt Welder, 1962.

me to change the laws of nature."[39] The chemicals, placed on the outside of a stick electrode, shielded the arc from the atmosphere and allowed its steel core to melt and fuse with the metal to be welded. Placed inside the tubular steel wire, the chemicals, upon coming in contact with the heat of the arc, blew the electrode apart. It was necessary to find just the right combination of chemical ingredients to turn this volatile mixture into a stable compound.

Shutt and his group persevered through years of grinding experiment and analysis. Each engineer under Shutt's watchful eye was required to keep a patent book and to write up every series of experiments. The approach, Shutt recalled, was a mixture of science and art. Day after day, Shutt read and analyzed the patent books and plotted curves. At times, some of the data gave him a tantalizing glimpse of a formula or new approach that would make Innershield the dependable product he envisioned. By 1958 Shutt and his group succeeded in developing the first flux-cored electrode. Its applications, however, were limited at first to automatic welding. The automotive industry, for example, used Innershield to weld sheet metal seams. Further development was necessary to slow the new electrode down to make it suitable for hand-held applications.

Innershield remained a tough sell through the 1960s. Although the new product offered the advantage of high deposition rates, it was expensive compared to gas-shielded welding with solid wire. Operators objected to the smoke and spatter it produced. Gradually, Shutt's team was able to increase Innershield's attractiveness as a viable alternative to gas by improving its tensile strength and ductility. He and his group established a "family" of electrodes matched to specific welding requirements. Shutt recalled that he depended not only on the ideas of his fellow engineers but also on "thousands of quick and accurate chemical analyses from our chemical laboratory and thousands of accurately machined weld specimens."[40] For example, to develop an Innershield electrode for welding off-shore oil rigs, he needed a new material that did not exist commercially.

He loaned Tom Black to Lincoln's small research department in metallurgy and asked them to create it. They doggedly experimented until they hit upon a formula with satisfactory characteristics. With their new material, Innershield development took a giant step forward in 1971.

The Innershield effort revealed the depth of talent at Lincoln Electric in every department. Jerome Hinkel, in charge of applications engineering, had the tough job of testing Innershield. Ted Ashton, who became vice president of machine and motor development in 1984, and Richard Siktberg took on the difficult problem of designing a wire feeder for the new "inside out" electrode. This effort began with a wire feeding test program that led to the development by Duncan White of a special compound that could be applied to the surface of the wire electrode to make it slippery enough to feed smoothly. With Ralph Samodell and Theodore Klinger, Ashton patented the LN-9 Preset Wire Feeder in 1977.

The manufacturing of Innershield presented equally daunting problems. "Our present problem," it is recorded in the minutes of the Advisory Board for 1962, "is to develop the process so it has more universal application and to reduce our manufacturing costs... as quickly as possible."[41] With each addition to the chemical formula to achieve a greater range of applications, production costs went up. At first the company purchased narrow coils of strip steel, but variations in the steel thickness, width, and chemistry produced breaks. It was clear that Innershield required a previously unimagined quality of steel, as well as new manufacturing techniques.

The Innershield effort revealed the depth of talent at Lincoln Electric in every department.

To obtain the ultra-high-grade steel Lincoln Electric required, George Willis went directly to Edward Speer, president of U.S. Steel. He convinced Speer to make changes in the way U.S. Steel produced hot-rolled rods. Lincoln Electric metallurgist Dr. John Parks was assigned to U.S. Steel where he advised the steel company on how to adapt its methods and equipment to meet Lincoln's exacting new steel requirements.[42] Louis Bauman, then general foreman and later senior vice president of manufacturing, successfully set up experimental assembly lines to use hot-rolled rod as feedstock. An open "U tube" was formed in a series of specially designed rolling mills. The open tube was then filled with a chemical mixture, closed, and drawn down to the correct size.

Harry Carlson, Jr., then a young methods engineer, established criteria by which to identify steel rod with good wire drawing characteristics. Carlson had first met J. F. Lincoln while writing his senior independent study project on Lincoln Electric for The College of Wooster. After college Lincoln

Al Patnik (right) presents "orders" on a silver tray to Jack Munson (center) and Frank Boucher as they celebrate the largest sale in Lincoln Electric's history to the Caterpillar Tractor Company, 1965.

offered him a factory job. He married Marjorie Alice Morris, one of Lincoln's granddaughters, earned a law degree, and assumed increasingly responsible positions in the company. He became foreman of the Innershield department in 1965 and assisted Bauman in the transformation of the manufacturing process from a largely experimental effort into an efficient, standardized operation.

The years of intense preoccupation with the development of Innershield, and Lincoln's and Irrgang's refusal to consider developing products to be used in gas-shielded arc welding, had an impact not only on manufacturing, but also on sales and marketing. Californian Donald Hastings had joined the company in 1953 after graduation from Harvard Business School. He was just 31 when Lincoln promoted him to district manager. His district included Moline, Illinois, the heart of the farm equipment market. Some of Lincoln's biggest customers, like John Deere and J. I. Case, were located in Moline. The headquarters of Caterpillar Tractor Company lay a hundred miles to the west in Peoria. In 1963 ten of Hastings' largest customers switched to gas-shielded arc welding. To his consternation they threatened to cancel their Lincoln Electric accounts. To save this business, Hastings persuaded Lincoln to allow him to offer his customers L-50™ solid wire. This high-quality wire had a guaranteed chemistry that matched the American Welding Society specifications for gas-shielded welding wire. It differed only slightly in chemistry and diameter from the solid welding wire already manufactured for submerged arc welding. Caterpillar immediately placed an order for 3,276,640 pounds of wire and electrodes, the largest direct sale in Lincoln Electric's history. Lincoln certainly knew that the L-50 wire was to be used for the detested gas-shielded arc welding, but he continued to believe the company should not actively and officially promote the gas-shielded process in any way. For over twenty years, Hastings lamented, the inability of the company to refer to the American Welding Society specifications for gas-shielded arc welding wire in selling Lincoln Electric's L-50 wire, and the necessity for customers to adapt Lincoln Electric's wire feeders for gas-shielded arc welding in the field, frustrated Lincoln salespeople and put them at a disadvantage in the marketplace. Despite these handicaps, sales of L-50 wire proved enormously successful.[43]

A novel design for a highway near Red Deer, Alberta, Canada, shows the clean lines of welded construction, 1962.

Though it never became the all-purpose electrode that J. F. Lincoln had envisioned, Innershield's development allowed the company to emerge as the world leader in self-shielded flux-cored welding. The process proved uniquely suited for outdoor welding in windy conditions. It became especially popular for the welding of high-rise buildings in the United States and for offshore oil drilling rigs and platforms in many countries throughout the world.[44]

"BREAD CAST UPON THE WATERS"

In the period between the end of World War II and the mid-1970s, the welding industry, along with the rest of American industry, boomed. These were the golden years of the United States' economy and the spread of arc welding contributed to the ease and lower cost of all types of steel construction. The switch from riveting to welding was accompanied by changes in the appearance of structures. A weldment looked entirely different from an iron casting because it was constructed from steel plate and mill-rolled shapes rather than the metal cast in the shape of a mold. A weldment was also about 10 percent lighter.

During these years the company continued to spread the gospel of arc welding through its publications, seminars, and cash awards program offered by the James F. Lincoln Arc Welding Foundation. Charlie Davis's successor, Charles Herbruck, became secretary of the foundation in 1947 and served in this capacity until 1976. He edited the foundation's publications and two of James F. Lincoln's books, *Incentive Management,* published in 1951 (which sold over 100,000 copies), and *A New Approach to Industrial Economics*, published in 1961. Herbruck wrote a lively biographical sketch of J. F. Lincoln that introduced the 1961 book.

One of the foundation's most significant contributions to welding literature during this period was a massive reference volume written by Omer Blodgett, *Design of Welded Structures*, first published in 1966. Lincoln Electric's publications program did not directly pay for itself. In fact, many of its publications were given away. "Bread cast upon the waters will come back again," Blodgett explained, paraphrasing the Bible.[45] The company had faith that welding knowledge cast widely enough would bring profits back to the company over the long term.

Family tradition had shaped Omer Blodgett's interest in welding. His grandfather had bought his first Lincoln Welder in 1917 and his family, like so many other loyal Lincoln customers who placed a premium on quality, never bought any other brand. A modest individual who has earned an international reputation in the welding field, Blodgett learned welding in his father's welding shop. He graduated from the University of Minnesota in 1941 with honors in metallurgical and mechanical engineering. He spent the war years at the Globe Ship Building Company in Superior,

One of the foundation's most significant contributions to welding literature during this period was a massive reference volume written by Omer Blodgett, *Design of Welded Structures*, first published in 1966.

Wisconsin, as a welding superintendent where he used his expertise in arc welding to help train other weldors to build sea-going tugs and Liberty ships. After the war J. F. Lincoln persuaded him to pursue a career in industry rather than a Ph.D. in metallurgy, a choice he never regretted. During his long and distinguished career at Lincoln he was one of the pioneers in the field of structural welding design. He communicated his knowledge through seminars offered to engineers in mechanical and structural engineering. Started in 1956 and taught once a month, in their heyday these seminars attracted forty to fifty engineers from industry and shaped new thinking about structures that culminated in the publication in 1958 of Blodgett's *Design of Weldments*.[46]

The highway bridge program for President Dwight Eisenhower's Federal Interstate Highway Program of the 1950s provided a new opportunity to expand the welding field. The effort to promote welded bridge design began in 1949 with the James F. Lincoln Arc Welding Foundation's awards program, "Welded Bridges of the Future." The foundation provided the contestants with ideal bridge specifications. They were asked "to explore the future of bridge design unfettered by the restrictions of tradition that now limit work in their field."[47] From these contest entries, Professor James G. Clark of the University of Illinois produced *Welded Deck Highway Bridges* to assist structural engineers in their design work. This was followed in 1952 by *Welded Highway Bridge Design*, based on material from the second bridge award program.

At first these publications had limited appeal to conservative bridge designers who tended to stick with what they knew best. However, a steel shortage and rising prices in the early 1950s made designers more receptive to design changes that would conserve scarce materials. One of the former judges of the bridge awards programs hit upon the idea of making steel conservation the subject of the third bridge award program. Contestants were asked to submit two designs for bridges: one riveted, the other welded, and compare the cost and weight-savings of welded construction. The Rules Committee and Awards Jury included a number of bridge engineers from state highway departments. Gradually, engineers began to change the way they thought about highway bridge construction. A fourth awards program focused on the aesthetics of highway bridge construction. The series of books on welded bridge design prompted by the foundation's awards program culminated in the publication of *Welded Interstate Highway Bridges* in 1960.[48]

THE LEGACY OF JAMES F. LINCOLN

At the death of James Finney Lincoln in June 1965, Frank Ferris, still Lincoln's closest friend, presented the memorial service eulogy at the Fairmount Presbyterian Church. He made an analogy to the felling of a noble cedar that "goes down with a great shout upon the hills and leaves a lonesome place against the sky."[49] Ferris chose to speak of Lincoln's human qualities, but he refrained from picturing him as a plaster saint. Perhaps recalling the candor that sometimes got Lincoln into trouble with the press, he said: "He had faults and they were like everything else about him – big." Ferris singled out Lincoln's honesty as the quality that distinguished him above all others. "I have known him to make statements with which I disagreed. I have heard him make extreme statements for the sake of argument: he would rather argue than eat. But I have never heard him make a statement with an intent to deceive. More than once I have heard him tell the truth to his own hurt – though in the long run I do not think a man ever tells the truth to his hurt. For a reputation for honesty is a priceless asset – and that Mr. Lincoln had."[50]

Mary Grace (Mrs. Frank Newbury) is flanked by her two brothers, James F. and John C. Lincoln, early 1950s.

Ferris's eulogy contained many personal anecdotes, but he also revealed his knowledge and appreciation for the intimate connection between Lincoln's philosophy of life and his business principles. Lincoln had accomplished his mission to build the arc welding industry. He had convinced manufacturers, structural engineers, and the construction industry that welding was the "strongest, safest, most efficient and least costly method of joining metals." If "as it has been said, every institution is the lengthened shadow of a man," Ferris reflected, The Lincoln Electric Company was the lengthened shadow of J. F. Lincoln. Lincoln's labors had created wealth – wealth not only for the Lincoln family, but also for Lincoln workers. And that wealth had also benefited the Cleveland community that the Lincoln family had generously served for so many years. "Wealth is produced in but one way: by applying labor to material," Ferris noted. "Throughout his long working career Mr. Lincoln has been engaged in creating wealth by doing something that needed to be done and doing it better than it could be done in any other way." Recalling Lincoln's generosity to Fairmount Church and his gifts to a variety of educational institutions, including Ohio State University, Lake Erie College, The College of Wooster, and Fenn College, he said: "That the wealth thus created has been wisely and generously used many here can attest."[51]

"Throughout his long working career Mr. Lincoln has been engaged in creating wealth by doing something that needed to be done and doing it better than it could be done in any other way."

–Frank Ferris

Yet for all his enormous contributions to the company, Mr. Lincoln had lacked the will to step down during his lifetime. A complex man of vision, integrity, and good business sense, he had attracted a cadre of enormously creative individuals to Lincoln Electric and he had provided them with an environment and the tools to bring out their latent talents. But his determination to keep the company small, focused on manufacturing a few things well, drove away some people with ambition and executive ability. Buck Persons and L. K. Stringham had chafed at their exclusion from the decision-making process. Lincoln's refusal to allow the company to develop gas-shielded arc welding is an example of how his vision narrowed as he aged. Ironically, in *Incentive Management* he had recognized how difficult it was to "advance the able over the head of the old," and had advised in 1951, "Don't wait for funerals."[52] Only his death in 1965 allowed the company to be placed in the capable hands of his loyal successor, William Irrgang.

[1] Forrest Allen, "His World Is a Jungle" *Cleveland in Full Face*, 1954 reprint, LEC Archives.

[2] Quoted by Forrest Allen.

[3] Forrest Allen.

[4] Forrest Allen.

[5] James F. Lincoln, *A New Approach*, 132.

[6] Arthur W. Todd, "Basic Company Instructions," personal communication to author, about October 1992.

[7] Interview with Arthur Todd, Oct. 19, 1992.

[8] Memo T. E. Nicholl to Leonard Giles, Aug. 1, 1951. LEC archives.

[9] On the Linde Patent Case, see Transcript of Record, the James F. Lincoln Papers, Ms. 3569, Container 8, Western Reserve Historical Society, Cleveland, Ohio.

[10] R. D. Simonson, *The History of Welding* (Morton Grove, IL: Monticello Books, 1969), 142.

[11] Transcript of Record.

[12] Linde patent case news releases, LEC archives.

[13] Minutes of Advisory Board, Sept. 14, 1960.

[14] "Lincoln Explains Stand on Patents," [*The Plain Dealer*], Oct. 12, 1945.

[15] "Arc Welding is Being Handicapped," *Scientific American*, September 1947, 101-105. See also, James F. Lincoln, "Welding's Promise of Lower Costs," *Electrical Engineering*, October 1944, 375-377.

[16] James F. Lincoln, "Suggested New Welding Standards, *Welding Journal*, September 1950, 715-717.

[17] "Hearings before the Committee on Naval Affairs," 914. Also, interview with George E. Willis, May 19, 1993.

[18] Interview with George E. Willis, May 19, 1993, July 21, 1994.

[19] "How Lincoln Electric Pretested New Plant Layout with a Full Scale Mock-up of Production Lines," no date, LEC archives. See also, "Factory in a Stock Room," *Architectural Forum*, March 1950.

[20] Martin Greif, 96.

[21] Robert E. Hall, "Planned to Produce...," *Steel*, Feb. 4, 1952.

[22] William Irrgang, "Hairpin Hook with Built-in Hoist," *Flow*, May 1949.

[23] Interview with George E. Willis, July 28, 1994.

[24] "How to Move a Factory without Cutting Output," *Business Week*, Sept. 15, 1951, 82-84.

[25] Buck Persons, "Note to District Managers (To be given to all salesmen), Jan. 7, 1949. LEC archives.

[26] R. D. Simonson, 123.

[27] Interview with L. K. Stringham at Emerson Electric, by Jeffrey L. Cruikshank, Sept. 14, 1987. Courtesy of the Winthrop Group, Inc.

[28] Minutes of the Junior Board, Jan. 8, 1957. LEC archives.

[29] Interview with Jerry Hinkel, Feb. 10, 1993. Also, John Murray, Feb. 23, 1993.

[30] Letter from L. K. Stringham to Robert Shutt, Dec. 11, 1975. Courtesy of Robert Shutt.

[31] See L. K. Stringham, "Powdered Iron Invades Electrode Designs," *Practical Welder and Designer, The Welding Journal*, Aug. 1954, 788-89.

[32] The iron powder electrode was developed in Holland in 1944 and introduced into the United States by North American Philips Company. See R. D. Simonson, 147.

[33] J. S. Roscoe, "Iron Powder Electrode," Jan. 26, 1956, LEC archives.

[34] Interview with Buck Persons, retired Chairman and Chief Executive Officer, Emerson Electric, St. Louis, by Davis Dyer, Oct. 16, 1987. Courtesy of the Winthrop Group, Inc.

[35] Interview with L. Keever Stringham, Emerson Electric, Sept. 14, 1987.

[36] See Howard B. Cary, *Modern Welding Technology*, 2nd ed. (Englewood Cliffs, NJ: Prentice Hall, 1989), 8-10.

[37]Personal communication by Harry Carlson, Jr., 1996.

[38] John C. Lincoln, "Flux Holder," U.S. Patent #1,722,929, July 30, 1929.

[39] Interview with Robert Shutt, Feb. 9, 1993.

[40] Communication to author from Robert Shutt, Jan. 1995.

[41] Minutes of the Advisory Board, April 2, 1962.

[42] Interview with George E. Willis, May 19, 1993.

[43] Interview with Donald Hastings, April 22, 1993.

[44] Communication by Donald Hastings, Oct. 30, 1995.

[45] Interview with Omer Blodgett, May 4, 1994.

[46] Interview with Omer Blodgett.

[47] "History of the Lincoln Foundation," typescript 1978, LEC archives.

[48] "History of the Lincoln Foundation."

[49] Part of a quotation from a poem by Edwin Markham, referring to the death of Abraham Lincoln. Frank Halliday Ferris, "Address at the Memorial Service in Fairmount Church, June 26, 1965. Privately printed, LEC archives.

[50] Frank Ferris, "Address."

[51] Frank Ferris, "Address."

[52] James F. Lincoln, *Incentive Management*, 59.

William Irrgang, Chief Executive Officer, 1965-1986.

Chapter 6

Staying the Course, 1965-1986

MANY PEOPLE AT THE TIME OF LINCOLN'S DEATH assumed that the transition to leadership outside the Lincoln family would mark a fundamental change in the way the company was run. They were mistaken. President and general manager since 1954, William Irrgang had neither Lincoln's charisma nor prominence in the business community, but he shared his political and financial conservatism, as well as his operational focus. He accepted the position for which Lincoln had groomed him, strongly committed to the principles of incentive management and determined to keep them alive.

Like his mentor, Irrgang ran the company from the top down. He shared little authority with other Lincoln executives. He willingly listened to their recommendations, but resisted any change in basic direction or style of company operation. He was reluctant to consider global acquisitions or to expand Lincoln's product line. A man of few words and intense loyalty to the company, Irrgang relished his cigar, guarded his privacy, and savored the company's continuing success. For the next twenty-one years, Lincoln Electric did not change very much.

Under Mr. Irrgang's leadership, the company claimed a 40 percent market share of the welding products industry in the United States, forcing General Electric out of the welding business and reducing Westinghouse to a small corner. Lincoln workers continued to enjoy generous annual bonuses that in 1975 reached an average of 109 percent of regular compensation.[1] The outstanding productivity of Lincoln's workers allowed the company to continue to reduce prices, despite the scarcity of raw materials and their increasing cost during the double-digit inflation of the 1970s. A $4 million addition to the factory was completed in 1968 and in 1975 the company purchased another 107 acres of land in Mentor, Ohio, for future expansion. Demand for Innershield and Lincoln's L-50 filler rod, now identified for use in submerged arc and gas-shielded welding, proved so strong that the company built a plant on the Mentor site in May 1977. Even with the added capacity of the Mentor plant, it was difficult to keep up with the flood of orders for Lincoln's consumables.

LINCOLN ELECTRIC REVISITED

In the early 1970s William Irrgang gave the Harvard Business School permission to visit the company to prepare a new case study. At that time Professor Norman A. Berg and his research assistant, Norman Fast, were struck by the extraordinary continuity of the company's business strategy, coupled with its steady growth in earnings. Net sales and net income had increased steadily from 1935 while Lincoln enjoyed dramatically higher worker productivity than comparable automotive, heavy equipment and steel industries. Return on equity had remained steady at between 10 and 15 percent.

The Harvard study highlighted two statements, one made by J. F. Lincoln shortly after World War II, the other by William Irrgang not quite thirty years later. They demonstrated the remarkable continuity of the company's business philosophy. The 1947 case had quoted J. F. Lincoln: "It is the job of The Lincoln Electric Company to give its customers more and more of a better product at a lower and lower price. This will also make it possible for the company to give to the worker and the stockholder a higher and higher return." In 1975 Irrgang told Berg and Fast: "The success of The Lincoln Electric Company has been built on two basic ideas. One is producing more and more of a progressively better product at a lower and lower price for a larger and larger group of customers. The other is that an employee's earnings and promotion are in direct proportion to his individual contribution toward the company's success."[2]

The company's compensation policies continued to reflect the three key elements set in place by J. F. Lincoln: piecework, the year-end bonus, and guaranteed continuous employment.

Data published in the 1975 study contradicted the perception that Lincoln workers burned themselves out. Between 1958 and 1970 Lincoln Electric had employee turnover of generally less than one-half of 1 percent, compared to the electrical industry as a whole, which was never less than 3 percent, and to a national average for all manufacturing of more than 4 percent. If an employee adjusted to the rigors of the piecework system after the first month or two, he or she usually stayed. In 1975 the majority of employees had between six and forty years of service.[3]

The company's compensation policies continued to reflect the three key elements set in place by J. F. Lincoln: piecework, the year-end bonus, and guaranteed continuous employment. Indeed,

Lincoln workers appeared to thrive in the competitive atmosphere that incentive management created. For example, a veteran of the welding machine line compared his situation at Lincoln to his former job as a weldor for the unionized Cadillac Division of General Motors. Within two months at Cadillac he had achieved the highest hourly rate and could expect no increases in salary. At Lincoln he knew that the harder he worked, the higher his potential for earning. He said, "The thing I like here is that you're pretty much your own boss as long as you do your job." A worker from the Electrode Division expressed an appreciation for the financial independence and self-respect that the system fostered. His cash bonuses had enabled him to finance a house and he owned a car and a truck. "I wanted to use my drive for my own gain," he told Fast and Berg. "The money I get is because I earn it. I don't want anything given to me."[4]

Irrgang proudly asserted that stockholders had received an unbroken stream of quarterly dividends since the first bonus in 1934 with considerable stock appreciation. But the real winners in 1971 – the year Irrgang delivered one of his few public speeches – were Lincoln Electric's employees. Their bonuses nearly doubled their yearly wages. Their average take-home pay (wage plus bonus) was $16,708.00, making them among the highest paid workers in the world.[5]

The Harvard study characterized Lincoln Electric as a company focused on manufacturing. It highlighted a statement by George Willis (appointed president of the company in 1972): "We are not a marketing company, we're not an R&D company, and we're not a service company. We're the best manufacturing company in the world." Willis projected the continued worldwide growth of the welding industry and saw no limits to Lincoln Electric's size. Yet he also affirmed the *status quo*: "My job will still be just the traditional things of assuring that we keep up with the technology and have sufficient profit to pay the suppliers of capital."[6] That view would change when a severe recession and a race for global acquisitions tested Lincoln's unique management culture for the first time.

In the meantime, the principles of incentive management continued to hold the attention of The Harvard Business School. A supplement to the 1975 case study, written in 1978 by a young Harvard M.B.A. who had recently joined Lincoln Electric, compared coping with the company's demanding work environment to the pressure of learning how to prepare three cases a night during his first year of business school. Although not every new employee could take the pace, he wrote, people who stayed thought the money they earned justified the effort.[7] He linked employee productivity directly to Lincoln's financial incentives, commenting that at Lincoln it was possible for a janitor to earn 75 to 80 percent of the average starting salary for a Harvard M.B.A. The chairman of Lincoln, in his view, also received a good salary (about the average salary of a CEO of a *Fortune* 500 company). "But, one must remember that it is earned – the pace at Lincoln is faster than that at other companies."[8]

MR. IRRGANG'S TENACITY

Through the 1970s Lincoln's sales engineers saw some of the company's most loyal customers switching to gas-shielded arc welding. They continued to press for a full line of welding products – including those related to gas-shielded arc welding. Irrgang resisted, fearing the introduction of new products would dilute the commitment to the engineering, manufacturing, and sale of Innershield. The production of gas-shielded solid wire products remained the sole exception to this rule. In Donald Hastings' view, the most damaging aspect of Irrgang's refusal to embrace gas-shielded arc welding was not in the wire business, but in the limitation he placed on the range of welding equipment the company could offer. He instructed the engineers in the machine division that they must only design equipment that could be used for "our processes" – namely, equipment for welding with Innershield, submerged-arc, and conventional stick electrodes. Thus, even though the company was emerging as the world's premier producer of solid wire for use in gas-shielded arc welding, Irrgang did not consider this to be a "Lincoln process." The failure of the company to develop machines specially adapted for gas-shielded arc welding allowed Miller Electric, Hobart Brothers, and L-Tec to enter this market, creating a legacy of "fierce competition that could have been thwarted had Irrgang allowed development of machines for gas-shielded welding."[9]

No sooner had Innershield developed to the point where it began to come close to matching some of the operating characteristics of gas-shielded welding than competitors seized upon the idea of enhancing the gas-shielded welding process by placing some of the slag-producing and alloying elements inside a tubular wire. This hybrid process (welding with a gas-shielded flux-cored wire) produced quality welds with, in some cases, less smoke and spatter than Innershield. However, the company had to wait until George Willis succeeded Irrgang in late 1986 to change its policy toward products related to gas-shielded arc welding. At last given the green light, within a short time Lincoln engineers developed Outershield®, a gas-shielded flux-cored wire. Today Outershield is a major product line and The Lincoln Electric Company is the largest domestic supplier of both solid and flux-cored wire for gas-shielded arc welding.

On the issue of global expansion, Irrgang remained equally adamant. At the end of the 1970s the company's Cleveland-area plants generated about 90 percent of its sales volume. Its three subsidiaries in Canada, Australia, and France, together with its international distributor, Armco International, produced the remaining 10 percent. Irrgang's experience with inflation in Germany in the 1920s made him reluctant to invest any of Lincoln's assets abroad. He distrusted any economy other than that of his adopted country.

> Since Armco assumed all the administrative burdens of export and the problems of international exchange, the arrangement offered Lincoln a way to distribute its products throughout the world with minimal effort.

Armco, a subsidiary of the Armco Steel Corporation in Middletown, Ohio, manufactured Lincoln electrodes and flux under license in Sao Paulo, Brazil; Buenos Aires, Argentina; Valencia, Venezuela; Mexico City, Mexico; and Busalla, Italy. It had also created a network of sixty-three world sales distributors and forty warehouses. The relationship between Armco and Lincoln Electric, formed in the 1930s, had served both companies well. In the two decades following World War II, the protection of Lincoln's patent on agglomerated flux had given Armco a global marketing presence. Since Armco assumed all the administrative burdens of export and the problems of international exchange, the arrangement offered Lincoln a way to distribute its products throughout the world with minimal effort.[10]

Like J. F. Lincoln, Irrgang left the company's subsidiaries largely in the hands of the men who ran them. Though the Canadian and Australian subsidiaries were profitable, the performance of Lincoln's plant in France – complicated by the company's relationship with Armco – was disappointing. J. F. Lincoln had set up the French subsidiary in Paris in 1953 to manufacture flux and filler rod for Armco to sell. In about 1955 J. F. Lincoln committed funds to build a new plant in Rouen, completed in 1957. Proctor Ferris, the son of Dr. Frank Ferris, pastor of Fairmount Presbyterian Church and J. F. Lincoln's closest friend, headed the French operation. He submitted a monthly report, purchased equipment, and paid an engineering fee and year-end dividends to the parent company out of its very modest profits.

The Rouen plant had 100 employees at its peak, with three shifts in the flux division, as well as electrode and welder assembly lines. There was no union. Ferris, who spoke fluent French, introduced the principles of incentive management to his French workers, including a small year-end bonus, usually between 7 percent and 33 percent of regular earnings. He also attracted a group of very capable French engineers, some of whom had trained at the prestigious *École Polytechnique.*

The Armco relationship and lack of direct financial support from the parent company prevented Ferris from realizing the potential market for Lincoln's products – a time of high demand for welding products as Europeans rebuilt their cities after World War II. Armco acted as the sole European distributor for Lincoln's agglomerated flux, but failed to market other Lincoln products aggressively, convinced that for most steel fabrication and maintenance jobs, European weldors preferred rutile and low hydrogen electrodes produced by European competitors. Rutile electrodes had a coating that produced a soft arc and a smooth weld that pleased the craft instincts of European weldors. They were also smaller in diameter, a preference in European countries with high energy costs.

During the construction of pipelines in France, Italy, Belgium, and the Netherlands, Europeans discovered Fleetweld 5-P. Despite its smoke and spatter, Fleetweld 5-P's speed, high deposition rates, and ability to dig through rust and dirt helped to build a group of loyal customers and also created a demand for Lincoln's diesel welding machines, first imported from the Australian plant.

Inflation and recession in Europe, along with the militant unionism of the early 1970s, made management of the French plant even more difficult.

In the late 1950s the French plant expanded to include welding machine assembly, manufacture of Fleetweld 5-P, as well as flux. However, the real money-maker in Europe continued to be Lincoln's agglomerated flux. Armco's reluctance to distribute the full range of Lincoln products forced the company to set up its own direct-sales organization to handle stick electrode and welding machine sales. The expense of maintaining a separate sales organization for products with limited appeal in Europe proved to be prohibitive. Inflation and recession in Europe, along with the militant unionism of the early 1970s, made management of the French plant even more difficult. Almost as soon as Jean Revelt arrived in 1971 to take over as head of the French plant, Lincoln workers formed unions and went on strike. Equally serious was the rapid acceptance of MIG welding in Europe. Revelt recalled that because Europeans favored the small-diameter rutile electrodes with their soft, smooth arc, they immediately liked the small diameter of MIG wire and the ease of working with it. The European market seemed to switch to MIG welding overnight.[11]

The misadventures of the French plant did not entirely turn William Irrgang against expanding the market for Lincoln products in Europe. In 1972, when offered the opportunity for a joint venture with Big Three Industries in Scotland, Irrgang seized it. Ever cautious, however, he left the controlling interest and management of Big Three Lincoln (UK) Ltd., in the hands of Harry K. Smith, who headed Houston-based Big Three Industries, still the company's largest distributorship of arc welding products.

This joint venture represented a continuation of the relationship between the two companies that dated from the 1920s. Smith, son of the founder of Big Three, and Irrgang served on each other's boards. Big Three and Lincoln Electric had jointly bought a distributorship in New Orleans and a small packaged air reduction unit in Alaska. Their more ambitious joint venture in Scotland occurred at the time of the development of offshore oil drilling in the North Sea. The construction of offshore rigs seemed an ideal application for Innershield, where battling the wind off the North Sea made gas-shielded welding extremely difficult. Smith had intended to offer the gamut of welding supplies in Scotland. When British Oxygen Company (BOC) refused to sell cylinders of gas to Big Three Lincoln, this seemed to confirm the wisdom of Irrgang's (and ultimately J. F. Lincoln's) decision not to develop products that depended on gas.

While relations with Big Three continued to flourish during this period, the company's relationship with Armco began to founder. When Irrgang sent George Willis to take a closer look at Lincoln's international operations in 1977, he discovered that the high prices charged by Armco for Lincoln's agglomerated flux, no longer protected by a patent, had opened the door to competitors. This problem was particularly acute in Latin America – previously a Lincoln stronghold where Armco manufactured both flux and stick electrodes. Willis came home from that trip convinced that the relationship with Armco had become a liability. "From 1978 on," he recalled, "I had told Mr. Irrgang in different ways that we had to get out in the world." Irrgang listened politely, but took no action.[12]

As Armco International weakened abroad, at home the parent company, Armco Steel, like other American steel companies, had to reckon with competition from cheaper foreign steel imports. To raise cash to diversify in the early 1970s, Armco began to sell its manufacturing plants abroad, especially in Latin America. Fearing that they would be bought by international welding competitors, Willis and William Miskoe, vice president and director of international operations, urged Irrgang to buy these plants from Armco. They were particularly concerned because Armco's profitable Brazilian manufacturing operations reflected some of Lincoln's most advanced technology. They watched with dismay as the British Oxygen Company (BOC), a European competitor with a foothold in the United States market through its Airco subsidiary, bought two Armco operations there.

Even more serious was the aggressive strategy of ESAB AB, located in Gothenberg, Sweden. ESAB, the only major European company focused entirely on welding, had a history in the arc welding field as long and distinguished as Lincoln Electric's. However, unlike Lincoln Electric, which had posted a strong record of profits through the 1970s, ESAB had experienced the crippling effects of the 1974 oil crisis and its impact on the shipbuilding industry, ESAB's principal customer.

It foundered badly, posting losses between 1977 and 1979. New leadership in 1980 infused the company with a bold strategy to dominate the welding market through acquisitions in Europe and other parts of the world. Its most important acquisitions were the European welding and cutting divisions of British Oxygen Company (BOC), GKN, and Philips Welding Industries (Europe), along with their subsidiaries and distributors. Most of the troubled companies that ESAB acquired at bargain prices in the early 1980s involved welding consumables, although ESAB also picked up some gas cutting and arc welding equipment manufacturers. These acquisitions gave ESAB a strong presence in Scandinavia, the United Kingdom, the Netherlands, Spain, and Latin America. ESAB closed many of the factories it acquired to achieve economies of scale and lower administrative costs, but retained brand names and left distribution networks undisturbed. This strategy of buying market share through acquisitions restored ESAB's profitability and turned it into a formidable global competitor.[13]

Willis tried to convince Irrgang that to prevent global competitors like ESAB from selling consumables in the United States at artificially low prices, Lincoln needed to be able to manufacture abroad.[14] Willis was confident that the manufacturing efficiencies achieved through incentive management could give Lincoln Electric the same competitive advantage abroad that it enjoyed in the United States.

Between 1982 and 1985, despite the example of ESAB, Irrgang remained adamantly opposed to expanding Lincoln Electric internationally.[15] He made an exception in 1979 when he authorized William Miskoe to buy Armco's ailing distributorship in Japan and team up with a Japanese distributor, Aichi Sangyo. Aichi Sangyo proved far better at marketing Lincoln products than Armco, but it was difficult to persuade other Japanese distributors to carry Lincoln products. After the steel companies Nippon and Sumitomo turned down an offer for a joint venture with Lincoln Electric in 1984, Irrgang authorized Willis to look for a suitable site for manufacturing. The company completed the construction of a plant in Kobe in the late 1980s, but the increase in the value of the Yen and the difficulty of finding other distributors willing to stock Lincoln products made manufacturing in Japan problematic. The plant is now closed.

Though profits continued to climb under Irrgang's leadership, growth in the American welding industry had begun to taper off. By the 1970s welding was considered a mature industry. It reflected trends in steel consumption, declining in the United States and Europe since World War II.[16] The company continued to do what it had always done so well – manufacture a better and better product to sell to more and more customers at lower and lower prices. By 1979 the company had nearly a one-year backlog in some products. Two years later Lincoln Electric posted record earnings and

Employees of The Lincoln Electric Company voluntarily left factory employment to become sales support people during a recession that lasted more than five years, 1982.

paid the largest bonus in its history. Then, during a serious general recession in the early 1980s, demand for welding products suddenly evaporated. Sales plummeted in response to what turned out to be an unusually long and sharp recession. The Cleveland area sustained a rude blow to its economy, with unemployment averaging over 11 percent that year. Suppliers like U.S. Steel and many Lincoln customers in the automotive industries closed their plants. At Lincoln net income declined 42 percent between 1981 and 1983.

The trauma of a long recession only fortified Irrgang's resistance to change. With about 10 percent of Lincoln's stock held by unrelated public owners, about 40 percent owned by employees or ex-employees, and the remainder under family control, the company had protection from the bidding wars and hostile takeovers that began to reshape the business landscape of the 1980s. If Irrgang, then seventy-five, had entertained any thoughts of retiring, the recession changed his mind. His strong sense of stewardship required that he stay on until he had seen the company through the crisis.

TESTING TIME

Irrgang usually refused to talk to reporters, but this did not stop outside observers of the company from wondering whether the company could maintain its envied dominance of the domestic market. Even before the precipitous drop in earnings, an author for *Crain's Cleveland Business* had asked, "Is the Spark Gone?" He characterized Lincoln Electric as a rigid company where "the system is everything and it is immutable – products, markets, and people that don't fit are out." He noted that Miller Electric had surpassed Lincoln as a manufacturer of arc welding equipment, though Lincoln still led the field in welding consumables.[17] *Forbes* took a more sanguine view of the company's prospects in 1983, despite the tumble in earnings: "In its reclusive, iconoclastic way, Lincoln Electric remains one of the best-managed companies in the U.S. and is probably as good as anything across the Pacific." The article referred to Harvard's Professor Berg, author of the 1975 Harvard case study. Berg had described the success of the Lincoln incentive system to a group of Japanese businessmen. "Their reaction was, 'What's so unusual about this? It seems to us like a typical Japanese firm.'" Yet even a Lincoln Electric spokesman conceded that the Japanese, with their emphasis on group incentives, might reject a highly individualized bonus system. Berg remarked that the system would probably not be successful in Europe either, because "Europeans seem to view it as a bit like American cowboys – it's a bit too rough."[18]

The recession of the early 1980s proved the ability and determination of Lincoln's management to respond creatively to a crisis. While other companies laid off scores of employees, Lincoln Electric kept its commitment to guaranteed continuous employment. Plant operations were reduced, employees were asked to work fewer hours, but no one was laid off for lack of work. Though average compensation for a factory employee dropped from a high of $44,000 in 1981 to $27,000 in 1983, this was still far higher than the national average of $18,400.[19]

An innovative program saved the company from resorting to layoffs during this period. Donald Hastings, then vice president of sales, sold Irrgang on the idea that the company could offer factory workers and clerks the opportunity to voluntarily "change their spots." Hastings dubbed it the "Leopard Program." When the program began in the fall of 1981, 54 factory workers and 14 clerical workers, selected from a pool of over 100 volunteers, took jobs as assistant salespeople. They launched a new product – an inexpensive welder (SP200). This was the company's first welding machine specifically designed for gas-shielded arc welding. Its small size and versatility appealed to small auto body repair businesses, local sheet metal shops, and small welding outfits. These were new customers the typical Lincoln sales engineer had never approached. The new salespeople, peddling a new product, netted the company more than $10 million in sales. In 1985, when business picked up, most of the factory-workers-turned-salespeople returned to their former jobs with a new appreciation for the problems and demands of selling the products they manufactured.

Donald Hastings, then vice president of sales, sold Irrgang on the idea that the company could offer factory workers and clerks the opportunity to voluntarily "change their spots."

Another initiative Hastings took during this crisis involved persuading almost 300 new distributors to stock Lincoln products. Hastings recalled that when he met Lincoln for the first time at Harvard during a recruitment interview, Lincoln had asked: "If you go to work for me, how will you cut my sales costs? I've reduced my manufacturing costs by almost 90 percent in the last twenty-five years. My sales costs haven't gone down at all." Hastings never forgot this challenge. Early in his career Hastings accompanied J. F. Lincoln to the annual convention of the National Welding Supply

George Willis (left), Donald Hastings (center), and William Irrgang examine the list of volunteers for the Leopard Program, 1981.

Association, an organization of independent welding supply distributors. Lincoln believed in direct sales, but had allowed Hastings to experiment with selling through distributors in his Midwest sales territory. Though Hastings urged Lincoln to consider using more distributors, Lincoln remained committed to direct sales.[20] The company's transition from a high percentage of direct sales to 80 percent to 85 percent of sales through distributors began during the recession of the early 1980s. The company instituted a popular course for distributors to teach them welding fundamentals. At this time, the company also introduced a five-year warranty on its electric motors, an industry first.

Despite Lincoln Electric's own struggle to remain profitable during the recession, Harry Carlson, Jr., then a vice president, was convinced that Lincoln's incentive system could serve as a model for other manufacturing companies interested in improving their own operations. He sold Irrgang on the idea of promoting the Lincoln system as an antidote to deterioration of the manufacturing base of the country's "rust belt." Richard Sabo, manager of publicity and educational services, told the author of a case study by the American Productivity Center in 1985: "The company realized that it could no longer sit, an island of success, watching the wreckage of its suppliers and customers wash up on its shores." Sabo's seminars on incentive management proved instantly popular, attracting more than 2,000 managers from companies large and small in the first two years of the program. Asked whether the Lincoln system was transferable, Sabo was cautiously optimistic. Lincoln Electric's solutions to the problem of worker motivation had great appeal, but they required discipline. Managers of other companies, he noted, seemed to find it hard to give up corporate perks like the company plane.[21]

William Irrgang lived long enough to witness the company's return to strong profitability, though bonuses never again matched those of 1981. Irrgang's resistance to change and his intense loyalty to J. F. Lincoln's philosophy and example gradually had become counterproductive, though the board of directors, made up primarily of family members and company executives, continued to back him. Harry Carlson, Jr., reflected: "What he didn't realize is that the system and the company are a living, breathing entity and he only allowed it to breathe the same way it did when J.F. died."[22] Irrgang's most important contribution in his twenty years of leadership was to safely and profitably guide the company through the transition from family to professional management after the death of J. F. Lincoln. But because of his uncritical reverence for the tenets of incentive management, he failed to adequately prepare the company for the future.

---

[1] Norman Fast and Norman Berg, "The Lincoln Electric Company," Case Study 376-028, Harvard Business School, 1975, 5. See also, the same study in slightly expanded form in Christensen, Berg and Salter, "The Lincoln Electric Company, Cleveland, Ohio," in *Policy Formulation and Administration*, seventh edition (Homewood, IL: Richard D. Irwin, Inc., 1976), 352-384.

[2] Fast and Berg, 3.

[3] Fast and Berg, 21.

[4] Fast and Berg, 6.

[5] William Irrgang, "The Lincoln Incentive Management Program," Lincoln Lecture Series, College of Business Administration and the Center for Executive Development, Arizona State University, 1972.

[6] Fast and Berg, 13.

[7] "The Lincoln Electric Company (B), " Case Study 9-378-216, Harvard Business School, 1978, 1.

[8] Fast and Berg, 3.

[9] Communication by Don Hastings, Oct. 30, 1995.

[10] Interview with Ellis Smolik, April 28, 1992.

[11] Interview with Jean Revelt, Feb. 6, 1993.

[12] Interview with George E. Willis, July 21, 1994.

[13] Risto Laulajainen, "The Quest for Global Market Leadership: Example of Two Welding Companies," *Professional Geographer* 4(4): 392-406. See also, "ESAB AB: Toughing it Out (A)," Case Study 9-188-005, Harvard Business School, 1987, rev. 1988; and (B) 9-189-043, 1988.

[14] Interview with George E. Willis, July 21, 1994.

[15] Interview with George E. Willis, July 21, 1994.

[16] See discussion in Risto Laulajainen, "The Quest for Global Market Leadership: Example of Two Welding Companies," *Professional Geographer* 4(4): 392-406. Laulajainen writes: "The sales of welding consumables, and to a lesser extent equipment, broadly reflect steel consumption. The relative shift of consumption away from the industrialized countries of Western Europe and North America since World War II means that welding companies domiciled there face the risk of being cut off from sizable parts of the global market. From a total of $11.2 billion in sales, the regional breakdown of the market in the mid 1980s was revealing: Western Europe, 16%; the Americas, 21%; Socialistic countries, 31%; and the rest of the world, 31% (Esab [sic], 1986, based on a consultant's report unavailable to the author)."

[17] W. Wesley Howard III, "Lincoln Electric: Is the Spark Gone?" *Crain's Cleveland Business*, July 6, 1981.

[18] William Baldwin, "This is the Answer," *Forbes,* July 5, 1982. See also, David Whiteside, "Why this 'obsolete' company is a great place to work," *Industrial Management* 41 (April 1986): 46-51.

[19] American Productivity Center, "The Lincoln Electric Company," Case Study 48, Oct. 1985, cited in Kenneth W. Chilton, "The Double-Edged Sword of Administrative Heritage: The Case of Lincoln Electric," Center for the Study of American Business, July 1993, 4.

[20] Interview with Donald Hastings, April 22, 1993.

[21] The Lincoln Electric Company," Case Study 48, American Productivity Center, October 1985.

[22] Interview with Harry Carlson, Jr., April 28, 1992.

New addition to corporate headquarters on St. Clair Avenue in Euclid, Ohio, mid-1990s.

Chapter 7

Building a Global Company, 1986-1998

GEORGE WILLIS'S PORTRAIT HANGS near the other presidents of Lincoln Electric in the company's lobby. The portrait of his predecessor, William Irrgang, provides a study in contrasts. Irrgang's full face and ample upper body fill the picture. He looks directly outward, a cigar barely visible in his breast pocket. Willis's portrait shows him seated in his study near a large globe. He seems more remote and pensive. The globe represented Willis's aspirations – his determination to transform Lincoln Electric into a global company. If Irrgang's mission had been to preserve J. F. Lincoln's philosophy to the letter, Willis tried to keep its spirit intact while moving beyond some of its more parochial aspects.

J. F. Lincoln had tapped Willis for leadership early in his career. He promoted him to superintendent of the electrode division in 1951, only four years after graduation from the Harvard Business School. After becoming president of the company in 1972, Willis had served under Irrgang, waiting for fourteen years for his chance to lead the company. Willis was named chief executive officer in May 1986, and his six years at the helm of Lincoln Electric marked the first deviation from some of the management principles laid down by J. F. Lincoln. Lincoln had believed in keeping the company small – focused on mass production of a limited number of standard products, most of which were sold domestically. The long recession of the early 1980s had convinced Willis that Lincoln Electric needed to become a global company and to expand its product line to include products related to gas-shielded arc welding.

George E. Willis, Chairman and Chief Executive Officer, 1986-1992.

Between 1986 and 1992 Willis transformed Lincoln from a company with five manufacturing plants in four countries to a conglomerate with twenty-two plants in fifteen countries, including Brazil, Japan, Mexico, Venezuela, and most major European countries. Annual sales jumped from $370 million in 1986 to $834 million in 1991, pushing Lincoln Electric into the ranks of *Fortune* 500 companies. However, while the company's domestic operations remained strongly profitable through this period, many of the acquired companies, particularly the company's German acquisition, posted serious losses. Decades of efficient domestic management and profitability had created confidence and complacency on the part of management that through their own imaginations, creativity, and energy, Lincoln Electric's management and employees could solve any problem themselves. The tribulations caused by international expansion revealed some of the limitations of the system that had served the company so well for so long. The effort to restore the confidence of employees and stockholders after two years of losses from its global acquisitions set in motion changes in company leadership. After Willis, Donald Hastings, then Anthony Massaro took over as chief executive officer. After Massaro had resolved the problems abroad, The Lincoln Electric Company began a critical examination of J. F. Lincoln's management philosophy. The process produced a reinvigorated incentive system appropriate for the global company Lincoln Electric had become.

GEORGE WILLIS AT THE HELM

In 1986, as soon as he moved into the CEO's office, Willis unleashed the company's research staff to develop a flux-cored gas-shielded electrode. After the trials of Innershield®, the development of Outershield® proceeded with relative ease. Since the chemistry of the core of Outershield did not depend on exotic ingredients, it was simpler and less expensive to manufacture. Introduced in the summer of 1986, it proved immediately popular. By 1992 the company had added almost 200 new products. Learning how to manufacture and market these new products challenged not only workers on the floor, but also Lincoln Electric's sales engineers, who used to complain they needed more products to sell. The company added gas cutting and gas welding equipment, as well as gas regulators, to its product line in 1990 through the acquisition of Harris Calorific (a former subsidiary of Emerson Electric) with manufacturing locations in the United States, Ireland, and Italy, and worldwide distribution. Interestingly, Harris Calorific was founded in Cleveland in 1905 after John Harris, a stove manufacturer, discovered that an oxyacetylene flame could cut through steel. Harris Calorific became a pioneer in the manufacture and marketing of oxyacetylene gas for welding and flame cutting. Thus, after nearly a century, the two premier companies within their respective welding fields were joined in a single corporate entity.

Willis also began at once to look for other acquisitions in the international arena. He was convinced that companies that depended solely on domestic markets risked being cut off from opportunities in other areas of the world, particularly Asia and Europe. Willis found himself enmeshed in a web of international mergers and acquisitions after Harry Smith, the chairman and CEO of Big Three and a long-time member of Lincoln Electric's board of directors, called him in August 1986. Smith informed Willis that he had just sold Big Three to Air Liquide, a major European manufacturer of industrial gases and welding products. Willis suddenly realized that the time had come for The Lincoln Electric Company to move vigorously into the international arena. He thought if Lincoln Electric failed to act, it risked being squeezed out of the global welding market as large international conglomerates like Air Liquide, the British Oxygen Company (BOC), and ESAB swallowed up marginally profitable smaller companies worldwide. His first act was to begin to replace Armco International, the company's world distributor since the 1930s, with a new network of international distributors.

In 1986, as soon as he moved into the CEO's office, Willis unleashed the company's research staff to develop a flux-cored gas-shielded electrode.

The sale of Big Three occurred during Lincoln Electric's negotiations with the British Oxygen Company to buy the welding consumables assets of its subsidiary, Airco, in Cleveland and Montreal. Harry Carlson, Jr., then vice president of planning, worked with Willis on the Airco project. Lincoln Electric agreed to continue to manufacture and distribute products using the Airco brand name. Carlson enlisted the aid of Richard Sabo and a cadre of Lincoln's factory workers to dismantle the Airco plant in Cleveland and move all critical material to Lincoln Electric over a single weekend. By Monday, the Airco plant was an empty shell and the new product line was up and running in Lincoln's Euclid factory.

Meanwhile, Willis asked for a meeting with Air Liquide officials. They thought the meeting was to discuss Lincoln Electric's three joint ventures with Big Three. Willis, however, proposed that Lincoln take over a controlling interest in Air Liquide's arc welding concerns worldwide. He ultimately offered a 20 percent ownership of Lincoln Electric to Air Liquide. "They were astounded," he related, "but they saw the logic in it."[1] During these negotiations in 1987, in anticipation of their future partnership in Europe, Air Liquide sold its Australian company to Lincoln Electric. However, in July negotiations fell apart when price, among other things, proved a stumbling block in the sale of a part interest in Lincoln Electric to Air Liquide.

About mid-1987, Lincoln also acquired a minority interest in Industrias Soldarco in Caracas and started building a new plant in Valencia, Venezuela. Other Latin American companies were added at that time: Equipos Lincoln para Soldadura in Mexico, Brasoldas and Torsima in Brazil, and the manufacturing assets of Armco Mexicana and Groupa Sigma Alfa in Mexico City, Mexico. In 1987 and 1988 the company acquired from Air Liquide the balance of the joint venture owned with Big Three in Alaska and Scotland, and an additional 2 percent in Louisiana, giving Lincoln majority interest.

Willis thought it was particularly important to position Lincoln Electric in Europe before the European Economic Community set new trade restrictions in place. Soon after the negotiations with Air Liquide failed, he sent letters to arc welding firms throughout Europe expressing his interest in meeting with them. These included Fronius (Austria), Migatronic (Denmark), Kemppi (Finland), Norweld (Norway), Thyssen (Germany), Cloos (Germany) and Messer Griesheim (Germany). Only Messer Griesheim flatly refused to meet with him.

Willis thought it was particularly important to position Lincoln Electric in Europe before the European Economic Community set new trade restrictions in place.

Norweld, located in Oslo, Norway, seemed eager to come to an agreement with Lincoln. Norweld's recent acquisitions of Weldro with manufacturing facilities in Sheffield, England, and Smitweld in Nijmegen, The Netherlands, made it particularly attractive. This acquisition promised to provide Lincoln with what it needed: profitable sales, good European-accepted products, and a solid base of manufacturing in Scandinavia, the United Kingdom, and on the Continent. Lincoln Electric acquired a minority interest in Norweld in 1988, periodically acquiring additional shares of the company until it assumed full ownership in 1992. In 1989 the company acquired K.D. in Barcelona, Spain, a company that produced welding consumables of its own design and welding machines under a licensing agreement with Cloos.

Willis set a furious pace. Lincoln executives, skilled at running a manufacturing company focused on the United States market, had little time to develop the expertise necessary to run a global company. Indeed, their strong indoctrination in the principles of incentive management stood in the way of learning how to deal with the acquired companies. Lincoln managers tended to have confidence in the Lincoln way of doing things and little tolerance for the views and experience of the management of the companies they acquired. A fifty-year veteran of the company reflected in 1992, shortly before Willis retired, "We're very impatient in many respects and we're also guilty of inbreeding. We expect so much of ourselves that we have what could be a handicap in expecting similarly of others who aren't running the same race, necessarily, or playing the game the same way."[2] No outside international managers were brought into upper management at this time because Willis never doubted that Lincoln managers could run the new companies according to the principles of incentive management. He thought the new plants around the globe would provide an expanded arena in which to practice them.

Willis laid out the "International Operations Guidelines" or "axioms" for operating The Lincoln Electric Company abroad.[3] Under the category of general axioms, he wrote:

A. High-quality, low-cost manufacturing is our creed.

We must be obsessed throughout the organization to design, manufacture, and sell the very best-quality products in the industry.

B. There is no substitute for effective cost control.

Quality cannot stand alone. It must be coupled with the most efficient manufacturing methods and a total commitment on the part of everyone to control our costs.

C. Profit is not a dirty word.

Profit is the resource that permits a company to serve the customer. Our goal is always to achieve a solid profit before bonus and taxes. Sales volume without adequate profit is unacceptable.

D. Mistakes.

Any worthwhile endeavor may entail making mistakes. Mistakes must be analyzed to prevent further mistakes. However, those who do not make any mistakes may be relieved of their responsibilities, since the easiest way to avoid making mistakes is to do nothing.

E. Ethical conduct.

Integrity is indispensable. A company's reputation for integrity is one of its most important assets. Since in any endeavor, the law should be considered a floor, our conduct must be on a level above the legal minimum requirement.

These axioms summarized the ideas of J. F. Lincoln that had worked so well for The Lincoln Electric Company in the United States. Willis wanted Lincoln's overseas acquisitions cast in Lincoln USA's image. He intended to have his international managers set up advisory boards, hire carefully, promote from within. They were expected to institute piecework and a bonus system to stimulate workers' incentive. Like his mentors, J. F. Lincoln and William Irrgang, Willis welcomed competition and he believed the incentive system could thrive anywhere, as long as national governments did not obstruct international competition with counterproductive trade barriers, regulations, and taxes. He wrote: "We ask that every government allow us to conduct our business on equal terms with our competitors... Lincoln intends to compete effectively on the basis of our technology, the quality of our products, and the level of service rendered to our customers. Government incentives and artificial trade barriers obstruct the creation of a competitive world marketplace."[4] It was a page out of J. F. Lincoln's 1950s script projected onto the global stage of the 1990s. However rationally and morally compelling its principles, the transfer of incentive management abroad proved far more difficult than Willis had anticipated. The strict rule of promotion from within made it difficult to find Lincoln managers with the savvy to deal with different traditions and cultural values. The inexperience of Lincoln executives with trade unions and lack of knowledge of labor practices and laws in other countries proved major stumbling blocks in the effort to integrate the new acquisitions into Lincoln's distinctive management culture.

The strict rule of promotion from within made it difficult to find Lincoln managers with the savvy to deal with different traditions and cultural values.

Willis was convinced that The Lincoln Electric Company needed a position in Germany to protect Lincoln's market in the United States and to compete globally with ESAB and Air Liquide. Germany's strong economy and its location on the Continent seemed ideal for selling welding products to growing markets in Eastern Europe. In the late 1980s Willis made overtures to Thyssen and the Swiss company Oerlikon-Buhrle, subsequently acquired by Air Liquide. Rebuffed, he began to court Messer Griesheim, headquartered in Frankfurt with manufacturing in Frankfurt and Volklingen – a company almost half the size of Lincoln USA. What made the company attractive was its market in Germany and strong distribution network in East Germany. Willis pursued the elusive Messer

Griesheim for two years. He signed a letter of intent in January 1991 and completed a joint venture agreement in May. No sooner had the papers been executed than the German mark plummeted as responsibility for East Germany drained Germany's resources, and the Persian Gulf War deepened the European recession. The German company, renamed Messer Lincoln, proved a liability from the start. Messer Lincoln's production workers did not have the same attitudes toward work as their counterparts at Lincoln USA. They had guaranteed continuous employment by law and the legal protection of large severance packages when laid off. With high wages and long vacations an entitlement, a Lincoln-style bonus did not give the unionized German workers incentive to increase productivity.

By the end of 1990 the financial drain on the company from the new acquisitions had affected Lincoln's overall performance. Net income dropped from $27.6 million in 1989 to $11.1 million, and return on equity dropped from 11.8 percent to 4.4 percent.[5] Lincoln workers in its two Ohio plants, nevertheless, rang up a solid performance and Lincoln's domestic operations remained strongly profitable. This situation put Willis and the board of directors on the horns of a dilemma. Should the company pay the bonus Lincoln's workers expected, despite its troubling financial condition? Or should the workers receive much smaller bonus checks, even though they had no role in creating the losses? A close observer of the company, Kenneth W. Chilton of the Center for the Study of American Business, described the situation in which Lincoln Electric found itself as a "poignant example of the double-edged sword of 'administrative heritage.'"[6] The values and culture on which the nearly century-old company was based were inextricably tied to the bonus. Up to the end of 1991, Lincoln Electric had been a company with no debt. Now the board authorized Willis to borrow to pay the bonus that its Ohio workers expected. Willis explained in an interview with Chilton in July 1992: "[I]n order to pay the proper bonus at the parent company, we had to borrow perhaps 20 percent of the bonus. We *really* highlighted that. We told [the workers], 'You have earned this amount of bonus.'"[7]

Viewed from the outside, the decision to pay the bonus appears an anomaly. But from within Lincoln Electric's strong corporate culture it seemed both appropriate and logical. As Chilton has observed, incentive management was built on a "reservoir of trust."[8] That trust permeated the company's corporate culture and explained the persistence of institutions like the Advisory Board that could be traced as far back as World War I. Lincoln employees had always worked more efficiently than their counterparts in the electrical industry because they had a voice in the company and counted on sharing the company's profits. Since the first bonus in 1934, the seamless relationship between owners, management, and workers had never been compromised. Neither Willis nor the board of directors could conceive of undermining this solid foundation of trust. Consequently, the next year, when Ohio operations were again very profitable, even though consolidated net income rose only slightly, the company borrowed once more to pay the year-end bonus.

The precipitous decline in Lincoln Electric's profitability as a result of these international acquisitions, particularly in Germany and Spain, set in motion changes on Lincoln's board of directors, previously made up of members of the Lincoln family, long-time business associates, and company executives. The new directors, who were added gradually over the next few years, included Edward E. Hood, Jr., former vice chairman of the board and chief executive officer of the General Electric Company; Paul E. Lego, former chairman and chief executive officer of the Westinghouse Corporation; Lawrence O. Selhorst, chairman of the board and chief executive officer of the American Spring Wire Corporation; Craig R. Smith, former chairman and chief executive officer of Ameritrust Corporation; and Henry L. Meyer III, senior executive vice president and chief operating officer of KeyCorp. George Willis, who had announced to the board's nominating committee in July 1990 that he would retire on July 31, 1992, stepped down.

The announcement that Donald F. Hastings would become the next chairman and chief executive officer coincided with the posting of third-quarter consolidated losses – the first in the history of the company. As the company's losses continued to mount, in December the company borrowed $44 million to pay the annual bonus, based on the solid pretax profits for Lincoln USA. The following spring Hastings announced the purchase of part of an Ohio-based company – the assets of the Delco Machine Control Division of Dayton, Ohio. Delco manufactured a family of cast iron motors with energy-efficient designs. Lincoln Electric set up a new motor division in a $44 million renovated building located across the street from the main plant in Euclid, opening the way for the creation of about 600 new jobs. This acquisition provided the opportunity to try out more advanced flow manufacturing and introduce team incentives as an alternative to piecework.[9]

RESOLVING THE PROBLEMS ABROAD

To buy time during the restructuring in Europe, the company engineered a $230 million three-year committed loan agreement with Society National Bank, J. P. Morgan and other domestic and international banks. In marketing the package to the world financial community, Hastings recalled that it was like "walking a tightrope across Niagara Falls," but he knew the future viability of the company hung in the balance. To reduce long-term debt, which had climbed to almost $250 million by 1993, the board of directors began to consider raising capital through a public stock offering. This initiative was taken carefully because of the board members'

Donald F. Hastings, Chairman and Chief Executive Officer. 1992-1996

awareness of the magnitude of transition that was taking place in the company and their concern for its effect on the incentive system.

More importantly, new members of the board of directors with wider experience in international business convinced Hastings that there was not enough managerial expertise within the company to tackle the problems created by the new acquisitions. To restructure the European operations, the board encouraged him to hire Anthony Massaro, a twenty-six-year veteran executive at Westinghouse Electric with extensive international experience. Massaro had earned a degree in chemical engineering at the University of Pittsburgh, and had attended Harvard Business School's Advanced Management Program. After signing on with Lincoln Electric as a consultant, he was named president of Lincoln Europe in 1993, then president of Lincoln International. From Goodyear, Hastings recruited Jay Elliott, an executive with strong international experience and another alumnus of Harvard's Advanced Management Program, to take over as the chief financial officer.

Massaro moved to England to run Lincoln Electric's foundering European operations. In 1993 European operations lost approximately $35 million. "It was obvious," Massaro recalled, "that something had to be done and done very quickly, or this had the possibility of dragging the entire company down."[10] With Frederick Stueber, a partner at Jones Day Reavis & Pogue (who later became a vice president, general counsel and secretary of the company), Massaro and Elliott presented the company with a plan for restructuring its international operations. In December the board unanimously approved the plan and gave them a green light to move vigorously to implement it.

Quickly the team moved to staunch the flow of red ink. Among the first actions was the closing of unprofitable plants in Japan, Venezuela, and Brazil, but the real challenge was the company's European operations. Massaro found that, in addition to the high prices and poor timing of the acquisitions in Europe, in some cases the acquired companies were actually competing with one another. The European operations needed to be restructured to eliminate duplication of products and personnel. After closely studying Messer Lincoln's money-losing operations in Germany, the new team recommended that it be closed. Massaro set as a goal reducing overhead throughout the European organization by about 20 percent. In addition to eliminating duplication of product lines, the new European management team rationalized manufacturing so that some plants made consumables while others made welding machinery.

The company put a professional management organization in place with the ability to apply advanced sales and marketing techniques. Massaro was convinced that for the European market, Lincoln Electric needed to develop more technically sophisticated welding equipment. Chuck Murray, vice president of sales, took charge of introducing the company's new product line. Though designed specifically for the European market, this new high-tech welding equipment quickly became a mainstay of American sales as well. The new international strategy began to pay off immediately. In 1994 the company broke even in Europe, and in 1995 the European operations made a profit for the first time.

INCREASING MANUFACTURING OUTPUT

Meanwhile, in 1993 CEO Donald Hastings turned his attention to Lincoln USA. His approach to bringing the company back from the brink of bankruptcy was to increase the company's Ohio manufacturing capacity by hiring a large number of new workers – a radical departure from J. F. Lincoln's insistence on a small work force. He challenged Lincoln's Ohio-based workers to increase manufacturing output. "I made the calculated decision to manufacture and sell the company's way into profitability," he declared, "trusting the Incentive Management System would pull Lincoln through."[11] In the past, the company had relied on manufacturing a quality product at lower and lower cost to satisfy increasing demand. Profits had come through increasing productivity and keeping overhead low. One of the drawbacks of guaranteed continuous employment was the disincentive to hire additional workers during periods of peak demand to avoid laying them off when the inevitable cyclical drop occurred. Even with mandatory overtime it was often difficult to fill orders during these peak periods. Although the company's seven regional distribution centers allowed it some flexibility to stockpile during slack periods, a backlog of unfilled orders often meant losing customers to competitors. To satisfy continuing heavy demand for Lincoln Electric's products, Hastings and Fred Mackenbach, then president of Lincoln Electric, decided to hire large numbers of skilled and entry-level workers. They asked long-time employees to assist in their training. The effect of the decision to "manufacture and sell the company's way into profitability" was to create a two-tiered system of workers. Long-time workers were entitled to the bonus, but the new hires, more than 30 percent of the work force by the end of 1994, had to wait three years for their chance to share in the profits of the company. This waiting period was later shortened.

In Rotterdam, Netherlands, the architecturally dramatic Erasmus Bridge features a state-of-the-art movable section, or bascule bridge, to accommodate ships. The bridge was fabricated using products and equipment produced by Lincoln Electric Europe subsidiaries.

In implementing this plan Hastings counted less on squeezing more efficiency out of an already efficient operation, more on increasing output. To keep employees on the job through the normal two-week summer shutdown, the company offered the incentive of an extra bonus credit, in addition to workers' normal vacation pay. That summer they kept the lines running seven days a week, through the Fourth of July and Labor Day holidays. Hastings expected an equal effort from the Lincoln sales force. He urged it to look for innovative ways to market Lincoln's products to increase sales. Lincoln sales and marketing teams succeeded in selling all the expanded manufacturing output.

Profits of Lincoln USA soared. Despite a consolidated net loss in 1993 of $38 million created by the drag of continuing losses abroad, the board of directors voted to pay $46.7 million in bonuses to Lincoln USA's 2,676 workers. The continued excellent results of Lincoln USA, combined with the turnaround in Europe, allowed the company to report 1994 sales of $907 million, a reduction of the company's debt by $37.4 million, and net income of $48 million. However, though the company had recovered, workers were aware that their bonuses had not. An undercurrent of dissatisfaction surfaced. The company's losses in 1992 and 1993, and the extraordinary demands in terms of hours of mandatory overtime and postponed vacations, contributed to the perception among workers that they had carried a heavy share of the burden to turn the company around. Because of the need to reduce the company's debt, the bonus pool in 1994 was far smaller than many workers anticipated. "A lot of people feel ripped off," a tool-and-die maker told a *New York Times* reporter.[12] But if employees felt short-changed, Edward E. Hood, one of the new board members, thought it was stockholders who were getting "the short end of the stick."[13] An article in *Business Week* suggested that one of the "country's oldest and most radical pay-for-performance systems" was caught in a vise. It reported that the company had hired a consulting firm to study productivity and base pay scales and predicted that raises in base pay, accompanied by lower bonuses for management, engineering, sales, and clerical workers, would follow.[14]

The need to rapidly expand the work force had also forced the company to become less selective in whom it hired. Since 1934 when J. F. Lincoln had presented workers with their first bonus, workers had sent their sons and daughters, nieces, nephews, and neighbors to work for The Lincoln Electric Company. Rare job openings never needed to be advertised. But in 1994, even with advertising, the company's personnel office had difficulty attracting workers with the motivation and character the company had always depended upon. In the fall of 1995, *The Wall Street Journal* reported that the company had screened about 20,000 applications for 200 openings for hourly workers. Few were qualified.[15] Retaining new hires proved as challenging as finding employees with the right qualifications. Lincoln Electric's intensely competitive atmosphere made initial adjustment difficult. Between 1992 and 1995 Lincoln hired more than 1,800 new workers. Of that number only about 800 made it through the first six months. Workers who came from unionized companies expected more breaks and a slower pace. But young production workers fresh out of high school also found it difficult to fit into Lincoln's entrepreneurial culture because, speculated a supervisor in harness assembly, "they don't work like people did years ago."[16]

Retaining new hires proved as challenging as finding employees with the right qualifications.

At the close of 1995, Lincoln Electric celebrated the beginning of its second century in business and a resolution of the problems its international acquisitions had caused. The continuing strong performance of Lincoln's Ohio-based work force had enabled the company to become strongly profitable again. A 7 percent increase in net sales allowed the company to top the $1 billion mark for the first time. Lincoln Electric had also succeeded in reducing its long-term debt through a public offering of 30 million shares of stock traded on the National Association of Securities Dealers Automated Quotations system (NASDAQ). To minimize the change of control, the new class of stock was to be non-voting stock for a period of years. This was a way of preventing the new stockholders from putting pressure on the company to increase the dividends and after-tax profits at the expense of the bonus. To further minimize the impact of public ownership, when the company made its public offering in 1995, only 12 percent of Lincoln's stock was actually put up for sale. Thus, the company continued to be majority owned by the Lincoln family and employees. The stock offering added $81 million in new equity. Stockholders again received their dividends and investor confidence, as reflected in the rising of the price of the stock, increased.

Anthony A. Massaro, Chairman, President, and Chief Executive Officer.

REAFFIRMING INCENTIVE MANAGEMENT

In early 1996 the board named Anthony Massaro president and chief operating officer (COO). He returned from England to preside over The Lincoln Electric Company – now an international company whose profitability he had helped to firmly establish. John Stropki became executive vice president. Stropki, an engineering graduate of Purdue University with an M.B.A. from Indiana University, had started as a technical sales representative in 1972 and had spent his career in sales at Lincoln Electric, serving as head of Canadian operations in the early 1990s. Massaro reorganized Lincoln Electric into regions with presidents for each one: North America, consisting of the United States and Canada, headed by Stropki; Europe, including Western, Central, and Eastern Europe, presided over by Chuck Murray; Latin America, consisting of Mexico and the southward regions, headed by Ralph Fernandez; Russia, Africa, and the Middle East, with John Weaver as president; and Asia Pacific, with Mike Gillespie in charge. Each region was given significant autonomy in dealing with local economies, currencies, and management practices. Headquarters in Cleveland maintained control over the company's financial, legal, and engineering functions. To make sure the company's engineering department reflected an international outlook, Massaro brought John Twyble from the Australian company to headquarters to serve as senior vice president of engineering and marketing.

Shortly after Massaro began his tenure as COO he asked everyone in the company to turn their attention to the problem of achieving a unified, incentive-driven international company. The effort to build a global company had, in fact, created two companies: Lincoln USA with its strong entrepreneurial culture and unique institutions, and the rest of The Lincoln Electric Company, consisting of acquired companies in Canada, South America, Europe, and Asia. Massaro did not think it desirable or even feasible to impose incentive management *in toto* on the acquired companies, but looked for a way for them to participate in a system that had produced such an extraordinary record of profits for the Euclid and Mentor operations. Massaro was strongly supported in this effort by David Lincoln, the most influential family representative on the board. To Lincoln, the concepts on which the company had always been based were simple: First, the primary focus must be to serve

The Lincoln Electric Management Committee in 1997. Front row, from left: Raymond S. Vogt, Vice President, Human Resources; Anthony A. Massaro, Chairman, President, and Chief Executive Officer; and William J. Twyble, Senior Vice President, Engineering and Marketing. Back row, from left: Frederick G. Stueber, Senior Vice President, General Counsel, and Secretary; John M. Stropki, Executive Vice President, President, North America; and H. Jay Elliott, Senior Vice President, Chief Financial Officer, and Treasurer.

the customer; second, people will produce at superior levels when they are properly motivated; third, management should be scrupulous in treating all the company's constituents with absolute fairness; fourth, extra productivity should be rewarded; and fifth, integrity must be absolute. In 1995, Lincoln wrote: "Incentive management is being challenged. We must retain its effectiveness at home, introduce it elsewhere in the world, and make it effective there... The basics of incentive management are as sound as ever, but their implementation must involve adaptation to changes in global conditions. This is a challenge to management at Lincoln, but one that can and will be met."[17]

Massaro's goal in asking for a comprehensive re-examination of the incentive system was to preserve those elements that gave the company its unique strength and character, while addressing the new economic and social realities of the coming century. A fresh look at what motivated workers, and at how to evaluate and compensate all employees fairly, was long overdue. To help guide the company through this process, in February 1996 the company hired Ray Vogt for the newly created position of vice president of human resources. Vogt had made a career in the human resources field, first at the FMC Corporation in Europe, and later at AM International-Multigraphics. The first thing that impressed him was the tenacity with which employees held on to the Lincoln way of doing things. He soon realized that the uniqueness of the company's corporate culture, embodied in institutions like the Advisory Board, and the intense loyalty of the workers to the incentive philosophy, were also part of its strength.

A fresh look at what motivated workers, and at how to evaluate and compensate all employees fairly, was long overdue.

Vogt's exposure to Lincoln workers also convinced him that they are intelligent, think for themselves, and are not afraid to take action. Dissatisfied with what they perceived as their shrinking bonuses relative to base pay, several hundred workers met with union representatives on a Sunday afternoon in early 1996. The size of this gathering impressed upon Vogt the urgency of the need to re-examine the incentive system. Vogt and Stropki met with Lincoln production workers from the Euclid and Mentor plants over a period of several months. Because they were perceived as outsiders, lacking experience in manufacturing, Vogt recalled, "we really took a licking." The dialogue that took place at the meetings between the two executives and Lincoln production workers helped to build mutual respect. These talks prepared the way for a more systematic look at the underlying causes of employees' concerns. Union representatives waited expectantly, but organizers fell significantly short in obtaining the required signatures to initiate a vote to form a bargaining unit.

To open a dialogue with employees at every level in the company, the company hired Hewitt Associates, a consulting firm with a strong track record in human resources. Hewitt brought an unbiased, outside perspective to assist the company in addressing employee concerns. The company formed focus groups made up of more than 200 people randomly chosen from a cross-section of employees, including salaried and hourly workers, pieceworkers, foremen, engineers, technicians, office workers, and people in sales and marketing. In addition to participating in focus groups, these employees were asked to fill out questionnaires. Executives and officers of the company also were interviewed to determine what business challenges the company faced both domestically and internationally. The process revealed that "lack of communication, along with uncertainty about the company's direction," had created a sense of insecurity for employees, particularly with regard to the bonus. One employee, expressing the independence and self-reliance typical of Lincoln employees, declared: "We need to know more about the bonus. You always hear rumors, but don't hear the whole story... My math is good – it's my money, I should be told."[18]

In addition to the need for improved communications, the study recommended four areas for closer scrutiny by management: base pay, the bonus, the merit rating system, and benefits, including retirement, disability, and health care. The company formed committees to tackle each area. All the officers of the company, both those who had made their careers at Lincoln and more recently hired officers, participated in conceiving and implementing the new "Incentive Performance System," phased in over 1997. The word "performance" was added deliberately to emphasize that incentives are based on performance, both individual performance and the performance of the company as a whole. "Incentive Performance," a new company brochure stated, "is an integral part of what we do every day – it's not a self-contained program or benefits plan that operates on its own. It's an integrated system that incorporates the work we do, the compensation and benefits we receive, and the value we deliver to all of our stakeholders."[19]

The Incentive Performance System reaffirmed the essential soundness of the system of management that J. F. Lincoln had inspired. The company emphasized that a revision of the system was essential to meet the needs of the current and future work force, as well as the company's ability to compete globally. The reconceived Incentive Performance System involved changes in four areas. First, it introduced a new formula-based method of calculating the bonus. Second, base pay was revised. Third, a new performance rating system was introduced for salaried and hourly employees in non-production departments. After a thorough evaluation, it was decided that for factory workers, piecework and the old "merit rating system" continued to be an effective and equitable method to motivate workers. Finally, after a comprehensive review of benefits, the company proposed significant changes to employees' retirement benefits, more health care options, and an improved vacation policy.

Both shareholders and employees could understand the objectives of the company and what needed to be done to achieve them.

As before, the Lincoln bonus remained the keystone of the incentive performance system. However, a new formula-based method of computing the bonus took the mystery out of the process of arriving at the amount of the bonus pool and each employee's share. In the past, the bonus pool had been somewhat arbitrarily determined and employees did not know what to expect. Now there was a direct correlation between the profitability of the company and the bonus. Both shareholders and employees could understand the objectives of the company and what needed to be done to achieve them. The bonus, it was emphasized, was not guaranteed, but paid only when the company's financial objectives were met and an individual's performance warranted it. The officers stressed that the concept of superior pay for superior performance remained sound. The new formula-based method of calculating the bonus is a step toward greater company-wide unity, since the performance of the Ohio employees is no longer isolated from global operations. Although 80 percent of the bonus pool is based on the performance of the Ohio company, 20 percent depends on consolidated results (the performance of the company throughout the world). The board of directors determines the goals and reviews the formula annually.

By early 1997 Massaro, now CEO, had begun to implement a new strategic plan that included acquiring companies making welding products that could benefit from Lincoln's worldwide distribution system. The acquisition in 1996 of Electronic Welding Systems (EWS) in Italy, for example, added

A construction worker uses Lincoln equipment and electrodes on the new Cleveland Browns Stadium, completed for the start of the 1999 NFL season.

an electronic inverter welding line intended not only for the European market, but also appropriate for other regions of the world, including the United States. In 1998 Lincoln Electric acquired three more companies: Indalco in Canada, a leading global aluminum wire manufacturer; Uhrhan & Schwill in Germany, a world leader in the design, manufacture and installation of pipe welding systems; and AS Kaynak, a leading manufacturer of welding consumables located in Turkey. These acquisitions added significantly to the range of products and processes Lincoln Electric could market throughout the world. The strategic plan also included a greater effort to form joint ventures and alliances in the Asia Pacific region, enabling the company to manufacture consumable goods within Indonesia, Malaysia, and China. To that end, in 1998 the company opened its first distribution center on the African continent, in Johannesburg, South Africa, and named a new regional manager to serve that key market. In Asia, Lincoln Electric launched a joint venture in Shanghai. The new state-of-the-art facility allows Lincoln Electric to serve the market in China, and at the same time to support U.S.-based multinational customers that have opened plants in China and other parts of Asia.

The third aspect of Massaro's strategic plan was to focus on enhancing the quality, range, and appeal of Lincoln products. Support of the company's R&D was increased in 1997. Over thirty new products, including new computer-based welding machines and the industry's first digital communication protocol, called ArcLink™, were introduced both at the American Welding Society exposition in Los Angeles and at the international welding show in Essen, Germany. Equally significant was the investment in capital equipment and know-how at the Euclid and Mentor plants. In 1998 the company spent over $21 million on modernization of plants and facilities in Northeast Ohio.

At the annual bonus day celebration in 1998 Massaro and Stropki announced a bonus pool of $74 million. This pool, the largest in the history of the company, was shared by 3,259 eligible employees. Massaro was especially proud that in a year of considerable economic turmoil throughout the world, the company stood firm on its commitment to guaranteed continuous employment.

After a century that has included distinctive contributions both to the welding industry and to management theory, The Lincoln Electric Company now stands at the threshold of a new era. As this history has shown, the company's incentive system – so intensely studied and justly celebrated by students of business management since the 1940s – evolved through time and continues to evolve. The Advisory Board, introduced in 1914, remains a vibrant representative institution that keeps the lines of communication open between management and workers. Piecework, introduced shortly after J. F. Lincoln took over the company, still motivates production workers to maximize their earnings. The Lincoln bonus, first distributed in 1934, still recognizes and rewards employees for

Lincoln Electric employees the world over bring a rich diversity of backgrounds, experiences, and abilities to the company.

Today Lincoln Electric workers are better educated, more diverse, and they work in plants around the world.

their role in generating the profits of the company. Finally, the postwar promise of guaranteed continuous employment still provides a rationale for job flexibility and promotes loyalty to the company.

J. F. Lincoln's mission was to contribute to raising the standard of living of ordinary Americans – people like the first- and second-generation immigrants he employed in his Cleveland plant. He thought the best way to achieve this was neither through private charity nor government social programs, but by promoting "intelligent selfishness." Motivated employees served their own interests along with those of the company. Rewarding them for their productivity with a cash incentive was simply good business. The incentive system represented J. F. Lincoln's best shot at making the American capitalist system work for the mutual benefit of management and workers. A man of extraordinary executive ability, he had introduced the elements of the incentive system over time in response to the challenges of war, depression, and labor unrest. He never claimed that it was an ideal system. Nor did he want it to be slavishly copied. Moreover, he always emphasized that companies needed effective executive leadership. Aware that successful companies sometimes become complacent, he wrote, "The leader must give a continuous spur to the organization."[20] To Lincoln, intelligent and courageous management was just as important as motivated workers.

J. F. Lincoln's other mission – to win acceptance of arc welding as an economical and safe method to join metals – he also achieved. He never presumed to have a global vision, but the ex-football star might have relished the rough and tumble international game and reveled in the possibility of spreading the arc welding gospel to people in developing countries. If the initiative taken by management between 1986 and 1996 to create a global company produced trauma, it also opened up a dialogue between workers and management of which J. F. Lincoln would have heartily approved.

The Lincoln Electric Company now operates in a larger and more complex world, but its corporate culture is still infused with the values J. F. Lincoln personified. Today Lincoln Electric workers are better educated, more diverse, and they work in plants around the world. The company's management is made up not only of men and women who started on the factory floor and worked their way up, but also of executives who gained significant international experience abroad before bringing their talents to The Lincoln Electric Company. As all Lincoln Electric employees carry the company forward into the twenty-first century, for them, as J. F. Lincoln used to say, "the possible is immense."

[1] Interview with George E. Willis, July 21, 1994.

[2] Interview with Ellis Smolik by Davis Dyer, April 28, 1992.

[3] George E. Willis, "International Operations Guidelines created to enhance worldwide subsidiary and joint venture operations," [no date], courtesy of George Willis.

[4] George E. Willis, "International Operations Guidelines."

[5] *1992 Annual Report*. The Lincoln Electric Company.

[6] Kenneth W. Chilton, "The Double-Edged Sword of Administrative Heritage," Center for the Study of American Business, July 1993, 1.

[7] Kenneth Chilton, 11.

[8] See Kenneth W. Chilton, "Lincoln Electric's Incentive System: A Reservoir of Trust," reprinted from *Compensation & Benefits Review*, Dec. 1994.

[9] In 1998 it was announced that the Motor Division would be sold.

[10] Interview with Anthony Massaro, Sept. 18, 1997.

[11] Donald Hastings, document dated Dec. 7,1995.

[12] Barnaby J. Feder, "Recasting a Model Incentive Strategy," *The New York Times*, Sept. 5, 1994.

[13] Ibid.

[14] Zachary Schiller, "Model Incentive Plan Gets Caught in a Vise," *Business Week*, Jan. 22, 1996. Thomas W. Gerdel, "Lincoln Electric experiences season of worker discontent," *The Plain Dealer*, Dec.10, 1995.

[15] Raju Narisetti, "Manufacturers Decry a Shortage of Workers While Rejecting Many," *The Wall Street Journal*, Sept. 8, 1995.

[16] Interview with Joe Kernya and Kathleen Hoenigman, Jan. 23, 1996.

[17] David Lincoln, "Postscript" [Jan. 1994].

[18] "Incentive Performance System," pamphlet published by The Lincoln Electric Company, 1996.

[19] "Incentive Performance System."

[20] *A New Approach to Industrial Economics*, 153.

Index

A

B

C

D

E

F

G

H

I

J

K

L

M

N

O

P

Q

R

Y

ABOUT THE AUTHOR

VIRGINIA DAWSON, PH.D., is the founder and president of History Enterprises, Inc., a Cleveland company that specializes in writing histories for businesses and non-profit organizations and setting up and maintaining their archives. She is the author of two previous books, *Nature's Enigma*, a book on the history of biology, and *Engines and Innovation: Lewis Laboratory and American Propulsion Technology*, published in the NASA history series. Local histories include *Hands on the Past* for The Shaker Historical Society, *Learning for Life* for Hathaway Brown School, and *Shaping Nursing Knowledge and Practice* (with Mark Bowles) for The Frances Payne Bolton School of Nursing. An article on E. G. Bailey, founder of the Bailey Meter Company, was recently published in *Technology and Culture.* Other articles have appeared in publications by the Smithsonian Institution and international journals in the history of technology and science.